THE LIGHT WAS GOOD

◆ ◆ ◆

-- to my former self who I love and cherish. Thank you for reminding me of where I come from.

"Can you understand? Someone, somewhere, can you understand me a little, love me a little? For all my despair, for all my ideals, for all that – I love life. But it is hard, and I have so much – so very much to learn."
~ Sylvia Plath

"I am alone here in my own mind.
There is no map
and there is no road.
It is one of a kind
just as yours is."
~ Anne Sexton

"For now she need not think of anybody. She could be herself, by herself. And that was what now she often felt the need of - to think; well not even to think. To be silent; to be alone. All the being and the doing, expansive, glittering, vocal, evaporated; and one shrunk, with a sense of solemnity, to being oneself, a wedge-shaped core of darkness, something invisible to others... and this self having shed its attachments was free for the strangest adventures."
~ Virginia Woolf

C hapter One

My name is Jane. I don't know my exact age, but I've reasoned it to be around nineteen. I have a small home near the White Mountain National Forest towards its northern region in Maine and I prefer to live alone. I have brown hair, but I keep it short, chin-length, and black eyes to match. I'm shorter and lighter than the average woman and my complexion is pasty. I think that should suffice.

I prefer curt introductions over detailed explanations because my likes and dislikes, ambitions, dreams, wants, are dynamic and stating them will only mark a static impression of me in you. My ever-changing selection of platters within this banquet of life will only tire you into considering me frivolous and I have no place in my life for people who limit me. I suffer around people who lack intuition or commitment, those unable to pierce into the soul of another, or those who hack away at someone's psyche only to leave the excavation site when it gets muddy regardless of the history hidden below. And I have so much history buried beneath my breast... broken ribs mark the entry of those who once excavated, but my history, their treasure, still lies within my chest.

That's another reason why I prefer curt introductions... I don't know who I am... I don't even know how old I am... What did those excavators find inside me that made them turn away? I can tell you what I look like, but I can't explain who I am. I was born and raised within a cult isolated from your world, surrounded by lies, fed by lies, and sustained by lies, only to escape. I stumbled into your world at the presumed age of thirteen. From there, I was carried into a little moving room on wheels by a nice man wearing a star, carried out of the little room into the tallest box I had ever seen filled with bright lights and sitting people, handed off into the arms of a woman wearing a white robe who placed me in my very own bed, wrapped me up in blankets, put a mask over my face, and told me to breathe. Ever since I woke up, I've been trying to make sense of everything. At first, I tread through realizations at a crawl, but as the chains which once bound my mind clattered against the ground, I ran. I ran through my memories, thoughts, and emotions without ramifications. I sprinted through every lie and suffered what they entailed. Little did I know, my upbringing had etched warning signs on my bones for anyone daring enough to venture inside me. Like forgotten axes absorbed into oak trees, I'm unaware of my ingrained faults.

That's why I need to write out my history... I want to understand what happened to me... and maybe then... others can understand me, too.

I want to make this analysis entirely objective, though. I've struggled through writing it before because no matter how much I distance myself from the topic at hand, I often get emotionally slaughtered when discussing it. I've been disassociating myself from my childhood, recalling the memories as scenes from a movie, endeavoring to avoid the plaguing anxiety attached to writing, but it's been six years since I escaped, six years of me constantly thinking, and I still can't manage objectivity over this topic. I feel like a hypocrite. How can I pretend to be so rational when my feelings muddy everything? Writing is the most efficient form of expressing what I remember while remaining as concise as I can, without sidetracking down some tangent or going mute as I did as a child, but this document cannot be objective. I'm an unreliable narrator. That's my disclaimer and challenge. The content I'm about to write will be true to my fuzzy memory. It will guide me towards a better understanding of myself, but it will be the subject of my mind and nothing more.

Officers and reporters ignored my claims about the underground, at first. They considered me delusional until the building was torn down and bodies were found crushed beneath the rubble. Ever since its discovery, I've had their undivided attention. If you're someone who's interested in knowing about the morbidity of my cult, then I need you to question everything I say. Reason for yourself the validity of my words and keep in mind the possibility that I might be, at the very least, off. I could say the wrong name, recall an imprecise dialogue tailored within a context I had felt it in at the time, and I could push principles I've developed throughout this account of my childhood. Learn how to distinguish the absolute truths from my opinions. If at any time I offend you with the gravity or severity of my childhood, then analyze the reason as to why you're offended. Don't sweep my experience away for the sake of sensibility. Otherwise, you'll miss valuable practice.

The doctors determined I was thirteen years old. They would've considered me eight because of my petite frame, but once they took into account my menstrual cycle, malnutrition, and lack of sunlight, they agreed upon thirteen. An age no child should be having a child, so they unburdened me with the curse the underground gave me. Within my childhood world, or the congregation as it was commonly referred to, we lived within a large, stone basement with thin windows peeping over the ground floor scattered throughout the halls and different rooms. All the windows were boarded up by molded, wooden planks and had curtains draped over them to further keep the sunlight out. The idea of natural light was both evil and dangerous to us. The Antifasi, which was our version of an anthropomorphic, metaphysical force, characterized by his omnipotence, omniscience, and pure goodness, to whom we devoted our lives to, had denied mankind the privilege of sunlight due to the original impurity our ancestors committed.

Legend says, the original impurity occurred at the dawn of mankind, Earth, and the universe centuries ago. All of which was made in a matter of hours. It was when the first man found the first woman's form so beautiful, he gave into his sensations and fornicated with her. It was consensual, nothing malicious happened, but their act wasn't what the Antifasi had in mind for humanity. They were created immortal, so reproduction was unnecessary and the two were threatening to spoil his plans. He wanted to clone them and populate the world with similar looking, like-minded, obedient creatures to his liking. So, the Antifasi threatened to make the man and woman suffer if they fornicated again, but his plan had already been foiled. The woman's belly began growing months after the impurity. Out of loving wrath, he took away their privilege to sunlight, made humanity believe in the evil of pleasure as retribution, ripped away their immortality, and warned them that the day they stepped into the light of sun, it would be their last day as human. Despite both being guilty of committing the original impurity, the people in the underground came to blame all women, and only women, for it. There were several reasons why they blamed solely the woman, but only one seemed the most cohesive for our society. If the woman hadn't been so beautiful, then the man would've never fornicated with her.

It was because of this conclusion that every girl and woman had to sheer their heads, ashen their faces with charcoal, and wear formless, potato sack dresses covering their shoulders down to their ankles. It was our way of hiding our temptations from the men.

Of course, if the Antifasi had informed the first people that fornicating would get them killed, then it might've restrained both parties from fornicating in the first place. Or! If the Antifasi had informed them, which he didn't, then the man should've had more self-control considering how his immortality was at stake. Or! Maybe the man shouldn't have been so beautiful in form either because the act was consensual. Maybe if he had been uglier, she would've rejected him. Unless, of course, he then decided to rape her, but this is the Antifasi we're talking about. He would've excused that. These were theories which tickled through my curious, child mind, but the thoughts always dropped like marbles clattering into pits of guilt within my chest... How dare I question the Antifasi?

The congregation was founded a little over a century ago. According to our mythos, we were the only people the Antifasi found worth saving. When the appropriate time came, after the congregation had proven itself worthy of the Antifasi's gifts, the Antifasi would burn our flesh, turn our bones into steel, our organs into stone, our skin into a shimmering, diamond exterior, and give us back our immortality, so we could walk beneath the sun without fear of our humanity dying. Everyone outside the congregation, the unworthy ones, were doomed to take refuge within the shadows, among the bloodthirsty creatures prowling the Earth called the Fos Terata, until the day came where the Antifasi would destroy those unworthy ones to make room for the worthy on Earth. Couldn't those people have taken refuge within buildings during the day and walked the Earth by night? Why couldn't the congregation walk outside during nighttime? It's a natural line of questioning, but there are explanations for both. We didn't know what buildings were. We didn't know we were living in the basement of a building. We thought the underground was a different plane of existence the Antifasi had created for us to dwell in and, for that reason, we weren't allowed outside- hence why the windows were *boarded* up. Firstly, we feared the Antifasi would equate us leaving the underground to us rejecting him and we didn't want to lose our privilege to immortality. Secondly, why would we exchange the comfort of our world for the horrors of the outside? Thirdly, we didn't want anyone finding out about the underground. It was meant for us and only us, so we couldn't risk leaving and having someone follow us back. And finally, if we had left, we would've realized the outside world wasn't what we were told it was- and the leaders of our congregation couldn't risk that. No one knew the exact origin of the underground and no one questioned it either.

I sometimes wondered why an omnipotent and omniscient force couldn't think of a better alternative to reality than a stone basement, especially since we were his chosen people, but I didn't have the courage to ask. I didn't want to get in trouble. Despite all the questions I had feathering my mind at such an honest age, I refrained from asking most of them out of fear. "Questioning is arrogance," my father, one of the four leaders of the underground, once told me when I was a little girl, "and unless you want to feel the Antifasi's wrath, you'll avoid thinking of them, Jane."

The Superiorii were the leaders of the congregation. Superiorii Faithfull, Superiorii Depherence, Superiorii Phorgiveness, and, my father, Superiorii Loyaltie. The Superiorii had male successors who replaced them after their deaths. Their successors were either their sons or, in only two cases throughout Superiorii history, their son-in-laws. Girls were excluded from any position of power, and discouraged from speaking unless in the company of other women, because of what happened with the original woman. How could men respect our power if we tempted them? But, why should we respect men if they only see us as temptations? We were expected to live in shame over what the original woman did to humanity- as if that was any fault of our own.

The Superiorii and their successors were the only individuals in a congregation of fifty or so people who knew how to read. From childhood, they studied the Den Amfisvito, a divine code of ethics the Antifasi gave the Superiorii to instruct the congregation, which their fathers taught them how to read until they could memorize the passages on their own. No matter what certain individuals, like myself, opined, the Superiorii were the only ones who could accurately interpret the text. Regardless of how foul an interpretation seemed, if the Superiorii preached it on the platform, everyone was expected to obey without question. Even if they upheld a rule which contradicted another or made a failed prediction, like their prediction on when the Antifasi would cleanse the Earth, they either pretended it never happened or claimed the Antifasi had not revealed the information to them clearly enough. Any dissenters, including people who acknowledged the Superiorii had made a mistake, were threatened with execution.

Every responsibility within the congregation, no matter how degrading, tedious, or abusive it was, was considered a privilege. Responsibilities for the successors included, on top of their studies, receiving food from the Antifasi and preparing it for the congregation. The Superiorii's responsibility, on top of educating their successors, was to lecture the congregation about mankind's history, the Antifasi's mercy, and the level of morality we all had to maintain and excel in. If the congregation, or just one member in it, wavered in morality, the Antifasi would choke the food supply. Sometimes the Antifasi provided no food for us at all, sometimes for days, but it was because we, as a congregation, weren't being obedient enough... or at least that's what the Superiorii told us... The Superiorii would then berate the congregation for bringing this famine upon us and encourage one another to keep an eye out on the flaws of others to cleanse the congregation of the food depriving source- someone committing an impurity. Paranoia would grow high until an accusation was made and followed up on. Whether it was someone's eccentricities, a physical defect, revenge, or sheer unfortunate luck, someone would be accused of an impurity, thrown into a furnace in the left room to the main hall, and the congregation would assemble and watch them burn. Afterwards, we'd eat again like nothing happened.

I can somewhat recall the number of executions I witnessed growing up.

Nine, I think.

It wasn't an annual thing, it was even considered rare, but in the last couple months prior to my escape, four of the nine people I saw burn were executed. Children were present during these burnings even if they were related to the executed- everyone's presence was demanded regardless of age or relation. In fact, one of my earliest memories was the first burning I witnessed. It was a man, but I couldn't make out his identity. I might've known him, but I was too little to recall. All I remember is liking the smallness of the left room and wanting to play house in it when no one was watching me. Then the screams were born...

He screamed through the gag the Superiorii shoved in the mouths of the soon to be executed and I wailed at his sudden shrieks. I was begging them to stop- stop the noise, stop the sight- but I could only manage an innocent, "*Stop! Stop!*" An older woman from the congregation tried comforting me. She grabbed my shoulder, lowered herself down to my stature, and told me the Antifasi wanted him to burn, but the spots on her hand only further disgusted me and I shook her grasp off to the chagrin of my father who was already embarrassed by my crying. From then on, a part of me knew the Antifasi was undeniably cruel, but my parents' and the congregation's conviction of his goodness made me doubt my own judgment. I was prideful, arrogant, evil, and possessed a dangerous mind. Every quality I ascribed the Antifasi reflected off him and onto me... How dare I question the Antifasi?

It was customary to announce the reason for an execution in a vague, theatrical manner prior to it happening. However, I was too young to understand what the Superiorii were saying during the morning sermon in which they sentenced that man to death, so I don't know why he was burned. He was burned alone, though, in the afternoon, after the morning sermon had closed as was the custom, so whatever impurity he committed, it must've not consisted of sexual immorality. Unless, of course, his partner confessed to the act and was burned in the furnace room on the right side of the main hall in secret.

There were two hallways leading away from the main hall. The closest rooms to the main hall on both sides contained furnaces. The one on the right was reserved for those who confessed to their impurities. The one on the left were for lost causes. For example, those who were caught in the act, those who committed heresy, and those who stepped into natural light. Committing heresy and stepping into natural light were unforgivable, so, unlike those caught in the act, confessing wouldn't save you from the left furnace. Those thrown into the right furnace still had a chance at a better life after death, but they had to prove themselves in the afterlife before the Antifasi. If they failed their test of loyalty again, they would be thrown into the realm of the Fos Terata. For those burned in the left furnace, the realm of the Fos Terata was their only destination. There, they would be strapped to a boulder, naked, unable to run for refuge within the shadows, and would forever have their organs consumed by the Fos Terata. It was rare for someone to be executed for stepping into natural light, though- so rare I don't think anyone had ever been executed for it. People who committed heresy were usually caught when they vented their opinions to someone they thought they could trust, but that hardly happened either. The most common reason for executions was sexual immorality. Whether an unplanned pregnancy gave them away or the congregation noticed odd signs from one or two of their members, the Superiorii eventually found out. Usually, though, one of the two lovers would confess out of fear that the other would confess first and be burned in the right furnace while the other would be thrown into the left.

That's what happened to one woman after her lover was burned in the right furnace. Her name was Sister Jill Obediense and she was burned in the left cage because her partner had confessed before she had. She announced this to the congregation, hysterically, hoping she might be thrown into the right furnace after her desperate display, but we weren't a democracy. We breathed fascism. Whatever the Superiorii said was going to happen, happened, and they said she was going to burn without redemption, damned to be eaten by the Fos Terata forever in her afterlife. Prior to her execution, during the morning sermon, the Superiorii retold the tale of mankind's origin. To spill vinegar over her cut, they compared her to the original woman and the congregation to the original man. They painted her as a temptress trying to poison our minds and bodies as she stood by, waving back and forth on the balls of her feet, hazed like a phantom. As some sort of warped, motivational twist, the member of the Superiorii giving the sermon, with pride and power in his tone, announced we were going to do what the original man failed to do when being seduced by the original woman. We were going to kill the temptress.

This comparison was changed when a man was standing trial. Instead of comparing him to the original woman, which the concrete minds of everyone in attendance wouldn't have been able to grasp, they painted him as a beast. They emasculated him, dehumanized him, considered him animalistic and disgusting. A freak of nature, a perverter of justice, an abuser of innocence, a monster preying on the souls of men like an evil woman, and a creature drinking their blood. That was his last identity- everyone he ever knew, his friends, his family, considered him a leech. The Superiorii would manipulate the man, slashing their words against his character, until he broke into sobs, showing the congregation how committing an impurity can break even a man, the supposed pinnacle of strength, down to tears. That's what happened to the third person I saw burned. His partner, which everyone found out to be another man, confessed first.

After an execution, the congregation would sit down to eat their daily meal of potatoes, sometimes moldy, bread, most of the time stale, and meat, always burnt. The meat was saved for rare, celebratory occasions when we served justice on behalf of the Antifasi. It was the Antifasi's gift for us. I ate the meat once, but I hated the flavor. The congregation loved it because of its divine origin. It was considered defiant and ungracious to not eat the meat, so everyone licked their plates clean. The taste wasn't for me, though. It was too smoky. I thought it was hereditary because my mother also refrained from eating the meat except on one occasion where my father forced us both to eat the entire confection out of the shame we were causing him.

My mother was Aunt Joan Loyaltie. The wives of the Superiorii were titled 'Aunts' since it was there job to over-look the congregation from afar. I was an only child. Within the congregation you were only allowed to have one child per couple. After couples had their healthy child, which most new-borns often weren't, further sexual contact between the couple was deemed vulgar. Most women died during childbirth which made the men's lives easier. If the woman didn't die, engaging with your spouse on a personal level rather than a purposeful one wasn't common. There was no connection, no love, so ceas-ing to make love wasn't a sacrifice. The men were allowed an alternative to satiate their carnal desire which was tolerated if they were discrete. The purpose of ceasing contact with your wife and taking the alternative was to eliminate fears of illegit-imate pregnancies because, as everyone there knew, children couldn't have children. Children were the alternative. Men used children. The culture among women, which was propagated by both men and women, was to wholeheartedly deny any inkling of emotion or sexuality. Some even went so far as to muti-late themselves to prove their convictions and a few, for some ungodly reason, celebrated these women as being feverous ex-amples of chastity. These mutilators were considered the ex-tremists within the congregation.

Superiorii Faithfull's daughter-in-law, Jeanette, whose mother died during childbirth and whose father was executed for sexual impurity with a girl who could menstruate, mean-ing she was a woman and couldn't be used as an alternative anymore, was one of the few girls who went this far. After Jeanette gave birth to her healthy baby boy, the successor to a successor, she sliced off pieces of her genitals and showed them as proof to the congregation that she had rid herself of want-ing carnal pleasures. My parents, Superiorii Depherence, Super-iorii Phorgiveness, their wives, their successors, and a majority of the congregation considered her psychotic, but Superiorii Faithfull, his family, and the rest of the congregation approved of Jeanette's decision. This was the schism within our once united community. The terrifying part about this difference in opinion was the minority's zealous ambition of converting the majority to their side.

My father was the strongest opponent against the minority's beliefs and would often contradict the sermons conducted by Superiorii Faithfull, and vice versa. This was deemed wildly inappropriate because the Superiorii had to agree in their theology. Superiorii Depherence was the quietest member. Whenever he conducted sermons, he blushed heatedly and would often swipe his forehead of sweat. When his wife gave birth to his successor, he became known for his desperate, sexual appetite. He was infamous within the congregation for exhausting the alternative... Superiorii Phorgiveness was the most tender and accessible of the Superiorii. Unlike the others, it was common to see him smile and laugh- an incredibly fatherly man. He was taller than the others with a bit of gray in his beard. Even by the outside world's standards, he would've been considered attractive, despite his malnutrition, and for that reason, the women of the congregation avoided him like the plague. I developed an infatuation with him. He was the only member kept from administering sermons. Superiorii Faithfull, on the other hand, was the most brutal, strictest, harshest member of the Superiorii. His voice was full, drummed, and had the same lingering force the scent of an alcoholic's last drink has over his breath. His sermons were given in a composed fashion at first, but often spiraled into fits of controlled passion. The same way most worldly dictators administered their speeches and with the same message, too...

Obey- or else.

His message was phrased in a nuanced way. Unless you were on guard against manipulation, his way of speaking resonated with you. He exaggerated and fabricated the current state of morality prevalent within the congregation to one heading down a path of total disinhibition. Once people bought into this selectively amplified reality, he proposed his path which would provide a heightened sense of acceptance from the Antifasi and eliminate the temptation of impurity by reforming the congregation into one that transcended physical needs. Using 'the alternative' would be banned beneath his reform. Children would no longer be abused. This, of course, caught every mother's attention. Superiorii Faithfull had, on multiple occasions, shown his disapproval towards using the alternative and would often humiliate Superiorii Depherence in public for it. The women in the congregation weren't as opposed to Superiorii Faithfull's reforms as the men were. In fact, they supported him in silence. The men found the policies he and the minority were trying to push abominable. Not only was Superiorii Faithfull requiring, within his proposed reform, genital mutilation for women after they gave birth to a healthy child, but he also demanded men do the same.

Within his reform, Superiorii Faithfull required the congregation to accept a daily form of worship consisting of three sermons, one before breakfast, lunch, and dinner, instead of the one morning sermon. The idea of individual families within the congregation would be heretical. We were one big family that had to trust one another. Anyone found gossiping or slandering would be brought to judgement for inciting division within the congregation. But everyone was also expected to keep a wary eye for signs of impurity or lack of spirituality within the congregation. Anyone found guilty of not living up to Superiorii Faithfull's interpretation of the Den Amfisvito would be brought to judgement. The right furnace would become useless because those who committed impurities, even if they confessed, were not worthy of receiving a second chance. They would be thrown into the left furnace instead because they never thought twice of the impact their actions would carry, risking the lives of the congregation by eliciting the Anitfasi's wrath upon us, so why should the congregation think twice about saving their lives?

Few people accepted his notions as law, but the seeds of his reforms were still planted within the hearts of others who could influence even more within the congregation. They disregarded the horrors of his plan and focused on the beautiful details, but by doing so they put themselves in danger of wholeheartedly accepting a man that would bring about even more paranoia, morbidity, and fear within the congregation. There were no nuances to anyone's mentality. No one considered the possibility of pushing forth the desired changes into the already prevalent system and leaving behind the terrible ones. Maybe even going so far as to realize the conditions we were living in were horrible and proposing more ways to bring about a progressive change for the better. It was either one side or the other. The old way or Superiorii Faithfull's way.

By the time I was fully conscious of the world I was living in, I felt like an outsider. I hadn't even reached marriageable age, which happened upon the first menstrual cycle, when I was drained of living within a limited world. I felt trapped, but I also felt guilty for feeling trapped. In fact, I was terrified by my eccentricity, but I was even more fearful of what would happen if I expressed my guilt; I was sealed in limbo at a tender age. Another reason why questions, and curiosity in general, were forbidden wasn't because they were disrespectful to the Antifasi, but because they made portals in our minds. The Fos Terata could crawl and invade our world through these portals because independent thinking belonged to our impure ancestors. That's why those who questioned were burned. We were ridding ourselves of the portals they had created between the land of the Fos Terata and the sanctuary the Antifasi had provided. I was terrified my feeling like an outsider was a sign I was being used as a portal. It was a preoccupation that ate away at my energy for days, weeks, sometimes months after any question popped into my head, but, of course, if I wanted to stay alive, I had to suffer in silence- questioning everything, but never knowing the answer to anything.

The Fos Terata were either people who stepped into natural light, possibly including the first man and woman, or the souls of those strapped to the boulder who considered turning into a Fos Terata a better fate than being eating by them forever. The mythology was unclear, but for a human being to turn into a Fos Terata, they had to go through a process. After touching light, their bones would snap and contort, their organs would shift, their skin would rip and fall as their new form settled into place. Sores would bubble over their flesh like pockets of pus, most of them bursting, oozing from their wounds. A diabolical figure of multiple, wiry limbs gutting out from their anatomy in random spots like a squished spider. The bones in their fingers would lengthen, sharpen, and rip through their fingertips as claws. Needle teeth would stab through their gums, filling their mouths with blood, giving them their first taste for it, and in rows to better shred human meat. Their teeth were so sharp and their initial thirst for blood was so unquenchable, they would eat through their lips and the cartilage from their nose. Their eyes would boil until their veins popped, filling their eyes with blood. Their pores would open like a lotus pod and their hair, scraggly at first, would soon shed to reveal patches of torn skin left behind from their scalps. Their brains cooked within their iron skulls and the juice poured through their nose and ears each time they reached down to rip a chunk of flesh off their prey. Their bones would crack, break, or tear through their skin audibly as they walked and their stomachs were replaced by an empty void. That's what a Fos Terata was. That's what I feared was inside my head. What if my questions were the Fos Terata whispering in my ear? What if I was strapped to a boulder in the end? Or turned into one of them? The thoughts drowned me, but I kept my madness to myself.

I was the silent, avoidant child who knew her place as the eventual mother of a successor. I never once drew attention towards my position within the congregation or expressed a negative word towards anyone with anyone. My fiancé, chosen by my father, who would eventually become his successor upon his death, was considered an upstanding member of the congregation. He was almost twice my age, in his twenties when I married him at around thirteen, but never once had I shown my dissatisfaction with him. I accepted my father's choice of James Virtew for my husband when I was entirely infatuated with Superiorii Phorgiveness. It was yet another root beneath the immense tree of my guilt. No one suspected me of anything, so I was in no danger from them if I kept silent, but none of this mattered. I knew the Antifasi could hear my thoughts, both the rebellious and lustful, so even if the congregation didn't know my true nature- the Antifasi did. Even if I managed to avoid the left furnace my entire mortal life, I would still face his judgement upon death. The thought constantly disturbed me. It was my horror. My dread. My woe. It was a calamity I felt lonely in and which I brought upon myself alone, but there was one person within the congregation who sympathized with me. He guided me through my burdens. I reserved expressing the underlying reasons behind my pain, but I confessed feeling pain and that was enough for him to want to help me.

Superiorii Phorgivness was my confidant. There was an empty room no one used at the end of the right hallway we met in every night, when no one would notice our absences. We would sneak away from the rooms we shared with our respective families, meet there, and I would vent whatever I was feeling or just talk freely with him. He was my friend, my best and only friend, but I wanted to be more to him. I wanted to be his alternative.

C hapter Two

"What's troubling you, Jane?" Superiorii Phorgiveness asked.

One of my earliest memories is trekking through the darkness in the right hallway for the first time, wondering why I had been sent down there by myself. I passed by sixteen rooms, eight doors on the left, seven doors on the right, until I reached the last room on the right. The supposedly empty one I was told I could play in whenever my father was upset. I hesitated to open the door, though. I thought there was a Fos Terata waiting for me on the other side, drooling at the smell of my fear. Every time I was alone, that's all I could think. There was a Fos Terata after me, behind me, beside me, waiting for me, playing with my head, their food, and I'd never be able to escape it because I was a little girl. But I wanted to play house somewhere, so, despite my fears, I clasped the door handle within my dampened palm, clicked it, and gently opened the door with a faint creak.

When I peeked over the wood of the door and looked around, I noticed a figure sitting alone in the distance against the opposite wall.

The room was supposed to be empty...

I swallowed my screams, slammed the door shut, and scurried from the supposedly empty room back towards mine, down a long and never-ending passageway lacking in oxygen, my vision tumbling around and around in my skull while my knees jumped at each step, but before I could reach the haven of my family's room, I felt gentle hands on me. "It's okay, Jane," the voice assured, kneeling behind me, dunking my ears even deeper in his soothing, honey words, "I'm here to watch over you."

It was the first time I felt protected... and noticed... My feelings got in the way of my reason... I trusted the Fos Terata, knowing his sweet voice would crack into shrieks of starvation the moment I looked at him, but I was grateful for him having given me one moment to feel a warm heart. 'Maybe buzzing hearts taste better than broken ones to the Fos Terata?' I thought.

I turned around and let my eyes adjust to the pitch darkness of the hallway, fully expecting to see an abomination gargling blood before me, but the stranger was familiar. He was the man my father talked to after morning sermons. My father's equal, a man I wasn't allowed to approach or bother, and he was looking straight at me. The intensity in his eyes, his foreign presence, I was being noticed too much- I started shaking. I couldn't help it. Whenever I'm uncomfortable I shake. It only gets worse if I try talking about my feelings, but if someone speaks to me or looks at me for too long, I tense up and my body starts reacting to the overwhelming attention. It's a horribly embarrassing habit and I've done my best to get rid of it, but the only way I can avoid shaking is by avoiding any social interaction.

Without saying anything, Superiorii Phorgiveness let his hands drop down to my elbows and started brushing my arms up and down. Up and down. Up and down. His pace was like an afternoon wind blowing through fresh leaves in spring. Unrushed, but purposeful. When he felt my shoulders tremble beneath his grasp, he knew the cure to my shivering, "Breathe, Jane," he guided, "Breathe..." and I did. I took one, two, three quick breaths before he told me to breathe again and breathe more deeply which I did. "Do you want to go back into the room with me, Jane?" he asked, still rubbing his hands against my arms, smoothing the shivers out of them, "You can do anything you feel like doing and I won't get mad." His eyes were sapphire blue, warm and full of depth like brown eyes, but still insightful. They were the most beautiful shade I'd ever seen and he was still looking at me. Only at me. I smiled when he smiled and nodded my head. I wanted to go back into the room with him. I wanted to go anywhere he went. All I wanted was to be with him.

That was how I met Superiorii Phorgiveness.

"I already told you, Superiorii Phorgiveness," I answered, "I don't feel well... emotionally... I feel like... my ribs are pinching my heart and... I don't know... I don't know why I'm feeling like this..." I wanted him to hold me tighter and tell me he loved me. I was seeking his attention. I wasn't exaggerating or making up false claims, I really did feel like this, hence why I wanted his attention. His hot cup of attention in the cozy bed of his arms would relieve the chest cold of distraught I was sweating through. "...I just do."

"Do you feel guilty?" he asked.

Of course, I felt guilty. I felt guilty about anything. If I bumped into someone, if I spoke out of turn, I felt guilty. Nonetheless, I feared the admission of guilt more than the consequences of not admitting it. The Fos Terata eating my brain felt like a far better fate than losing Superiorii Phorgiveness. If I told him about the true nature of my feelings toward him, my feelings being deeper than a plutonic admiration for him, then he'd have to stop seeing me. He'd have to report my foul, demented state to the other Superiorii and they'd have to determine the correct course of punishment for a potential temptress like myself. If I told him about my curiosity towards the outside world, he'd have to report it to the Superiorii. If I told him how frequently and severely, I questioned the congregation and our laws, he'd have to report it to the Superiorii. There was no privacy in the truest sense. We were meeting within a locked, lightless room, furthest away from the main hall, but if I said the wrong thing, or the right thing using the wrong tone, then the congregation might've as well been present. I trusted and loved him, but I did so within the parameters afforded by our society. Just talking to someone about matters beside the Antifasi, our promised future, or the congregation was a sign of trust.

"No," I lied.

"There's no reason not to trust me, Jane," he insisted, "I'm your friend."

"But you're an adult..."

"And that merits a lack of confidence in me?" he playfully scoffed.

Despite differences between the outside world and the congregation, there were some similarities present. Children didn't know what ambition or responsibilities were. We didn't understand death. We were innocent and ignorant about our surroundings even if we were being used as alternatives. As a result, the adults saw us as inferior beings and treated us as such. Unlike them, we had no true purpose to our life except living it. The devotion to 'our', *their*, faith came with the time we had not yet lived. Until we were devoted members of the congregation, talking about how magnificent the Antifasi is of our own accord and how we couldn't wait to see him bring about our promised future, we would be inferior to them. That's why so many alternatives were confused when they were being used. They liked being noticed by an adult, instead of ignored and shushed away, but once the grooming finished and the abuse happened, they no longer knew how to feel about this strange attention anymore.

"But adults don't want to be friends with children," I said. In my opinion, Superiorii Phorgiveness was doing me the favor of giving me his company, but I never thought he considered me one of his friends. Friendship is made on equality, but we weren't equal. He was my superior.

"And children seek out the friendships of other children," he quipped.

I felt a sprinkle of panic spice over my heart when he said that. How could he mock me? He knew I was pathetic. A friendless child unable to socialize unlike other children within the congregation who did so with ease. Someone he was only spending time with out of pity, charity, maybe even guilt? He didn't know how to stop seeing me without hurting my feelings, so he visits this room nightly to avoid hurting me, but never because he wants to spend time with me. And my predicament was so sad and obvious, too... Being the daughter of a Superiorii meant you could make friends easily because you were in a higher position than most. People coveted power even children. They sought you out for personal gain or the betterment of their own image. It was a selfish definition of friendship, deplorable and unforgivably false to me, but it was normal within the congregation. People giving you fake love, fake attention, fake emotion for empty reason. It was disgusting. I couldn't stomach the duplicity of it let alone understand how so many people felt it naturally. How could they manage something so heinous? It's the worst impurity a person can commit... making someone believe you love them, so you can use them for your own benefit and toss them aside when they're no longer valuable... My foolish idea of what friendship meant, a deep connection rooted in pure emotion, was what kept me from making strong social ties within the congregation. It was a beauty pageant. A political game. People counted friends like points. Everyone used everyone for some means to an end. I was cordial to all, polite, correct, but only if I had to be. Otherwise, I avoided everyone. My habit, sad to say, didn't go unnoticed. I was considered wrong. Not my opinions, not my thoughts, but my existence itself- it was considered wrong. My avoidance limited the congregation's access to my 'resources' and though a few did try pushing me into a supposed friendship, bullying me, coercing me into admitting I was wrong about my isolation and they were the only ones that could help me be 'right', something I quietly believed in, but never admitted, my resistance against being molded into a concept more easily swallowed made me the least popular among the successor's daughters and daughter-in-law's.

Jeanette, Superiorii Faithfull's daughter-in-law, was the most popular, followed by Superiorii Phorgiveness's daughter, Juliet, who was a married mother like Jeanette, and then Julia, Superiorii Depherence's daughter-in-law. Joel Depherence, Superiorii Depherence's son, had a more voracious appetite for flesh than his carnal father did. The day after Joel and Julia Depherence consummated their marriage, bite marks, bruises, and lashes appeared on her face- the only visible part of her body. She was pregnant twice, but both were stillborn. Both sons. It was rumored Joel killed them to keep using Julia in his sadistic pleasure, smothered them in front of her, but I don't think anyone believed it. The Antifasi would've smitten Joel for killing off potential successors to the Superiorii line if he had committed the crime, but his being alive was testament to his innocence. It wasn't outside the realm of possibility, though. Even if they were stillborn, the stress Joel placed on Julia was what killed them. Despite the rumor, the congregation was silently relieved upon hearing Joel remaining childless because it meant their children were safe from being used as Joel's alternatives.

Although she married into a family of notorious predators, Julia was still more popular than me. She wasn't a judgmental person, so nothing interfered in her interactions with other members of the congregation and her silence was excused by the well-known abuse she suffered. I, on the other hand, judged people who I considered emotionally or intellectually stunted. If we didn't share similar perceptions of reality, in my stomach, I felt they were incomplete people. How could no one aspire to be greater than what they are? How could everyone be content with the superficial existence of reality and not delve deeper into their own or others' souls? My silence was attributed to my being insecure, but no one considered the possibility that I genuinely did not like them. How could I? If someone didn't have a tender soul to welcome me into, then I had no interest in getting to know them.

Apart from Superiorii Phorgiveness, I grew up alone. I preferred being friendless over socializing with others on their terms, discussing the congregation and how great the Antifasi was, how wonderful the Superiorii are, the same cult mentality which exhausted me, but I was alone more out of necessity than want. If I had it my way, I would've been surrounded by sparkling people who trusted, understood, and helped me develop my character rather than people who strived to mold me into another clone.

"Not everyone does what is considered normal," Superiorii Phorgiveness emphasized, "There are a few people who think for themselves, even if it's just to themselves, and remain quietly different from everyone else. *We* don't think the same way as the others do, so why should we follow their rules when we're alone together? We can follow our own rules, right?" he encouraged to which I nodded, "Right!" he cheered, "And who knows, Jane? Maybe you'll find someone your own age who thinks like you, feels like you, and is looking for someone like you the same way you're looking for someone like them... You just have to tread with caution and see for yourself who quietly shares your eccentricities by certain character clues."

"What sort of character clues?" I asked.

Superiorii Phorgiveness knitted his eyebrows slightly, enough for me to notice the cogs in his mind shifting and jumping into place to think of a way where he could eloquently explain the answer to my, what I thought was, simple question, "Well," he pursed, twisting his lips to the right side of his face, "if you lump my character up with the others and think you can't trust me, then even if I explained these character clues to you, you wouldn't understand what I was talking about. Right now, you're blinded by your general lack of trust towards people, so you'll have to realize these nuances of human behavior for yourself. Then you can distinguish who you can trust... and who you can't utter a damnable word to."

So, basically, he wasn't going to answer my question.

For all his kindness, Superiorii Phorgiveness was also the most intelligent and articulate of the Superiorii. It was this characteristic which struck me the most. I attributed his intellect to his extensive reading of the Den Amfisvito. He was a master explainer, often capturing the nuances of a question, he would give an in-depth, detailed answer which went above and beyond the questioner's expectations and left them with a sense of change. When he couldn't answer my simple question, I blamed myself for being too complicated for him. Why couldn't I ask simpler questions? Of course, no one, including him, a genius, was going to know the answer to my question because nonsensical questions have no right answers. Wrong questions always have wrong answers. I blamed my stupidity on my lack of education. Maybe if I'd been educated, like him, I wouldn't be so ignorant?

No one else within the congregation noticed Superiorii Phorgiveness's intellect because he didn't give sermons or contribute to conversations. He stood to the side, quietly, absorbing what everyone else was saying rather than speaking, so I was the only one who noticed, and fixated, upon his mind. I craved to be as smart as him, but it was too ambitious of a goal. The structure of my world didn't facilitate my dream, what with members of the congregation being barred from reading and women kept even more so away from knowledge, so my ambition weighed heavy in the coffin of my heart- molding, festering, with maggots eating the dead limbs of my dreams while it shivered half-alive.

"What sort of character clues do I have, Superiorii Phorgiveness?" I asked, fighting my eyes which wanted to widen in expectation.

I needed to find out what he thought of me, but I didn't want to forsake my true intention. Maybe he was in love with me? Did he even like me? Even if he considered me a friend, it wasn't good enough. I wanted to know why he considered me his friend. Why did he meet me here every night? What did he want from me? What was I to him? I thought my attempt would eek by unnoticed and he would blindly walk into my trap and give me what I wanted, *answers*, but, unfortunately, he had developed something I hadn't.

Intuition.

He knew I wasn't asking to gain a third person point of view on my character, but because I wanted his opinion. I wanted his judgement. Pitiful objectives to have within a friendship because it leads a person to change their character to gain the approval of their friend. But who wants a clone for a friend? If they can't support their own growth and accept who they are, flaws and all, then how can they help the growth of another person? Of what use are they? They're just the poor model of another human being.

"What's *your* opinion over my character, Jane?" Superiorii Phorgiveness retorted, smiling in his smug, but lighthearted manner. I knew he didn't care about my opinion. He was just teasing me down another long and winding answer.

"I asked you first," I defended, not wanting to honestly answer the question unless I knew my feelings were reciprocated first.

"Well," he thought, looking up at the ceiling, wearing this exaggerated pondering look fathers often give their children when handing them a decision, "I can either answer your question first *or… enlighten* you…" he smiled, pressing the 'l' hard against the roof of his mouth, "but it's your choice as to which question gets answered first."

I didn't know what 'enlighten' meant, and the fact that

it had the word 'light' in it made me nervous. What if this was a trick question? What if I picked the 'enlighten' option and it turns out I made the wrong decision? I didn't want to choose an answer that would put my character under question or, worse, drag the judicial attention of the Superiorii to my toes. I looked up at him, hoping he'd understand my confusion and define the word for me without my having to ask, but his eyes were pushing me into a decision. I was stuck. I didn't want to ask him for the definition of the word 'enlighten' because I was scared he might call me 'stupid' when it was his turn to answer my question.

"It's your choice, Jane," he shrugged, sighing out a breath of feigned exhaustion, "but I really rather hope we don't spend the rest of the night here, sitting in silence while you debate on whether you should ask me to define the word 'enlighten' or not."

He could read my mind! I felt a gong smash within my chest when the realization rippled through my chest, but my shock shapeshifted into horror when I reasoned what this could potentially mean for me, "The Superiorii... can read minds...?" I asked him, begging the Antifasi for mercy from the Superiorii in case they knew what impure cataclysms had been quaking through my mind this whole time.

Superiorii Phorgiveness burst out laughing, though. He laughed so hard he leaned onto me a couple of times which, granted, excited my hopeful, little heart, but I was also getting more and more hurt. All I could think was, 'He's laughing at my love for him... He's laughing at my ignorance... He's going to say, 'stupid and unlovable,' when he gets around to answering my question...' I even casually contemplated suicide as an option to rid myself of that humiliation. Run away. Escape his judgement. Hide in another world. I didn't even consider the horror of the Superiorii knowing my 'heretical' questions. No. The sheer embarrassment of not realizing the love of your life was reading your mind, hearing your every intimate, sweet, delicate, dirty, pleading thought about them, while you're sitting in their company no less, and them now laughing in your face over it was just cause for me wanting to kill myself.

"So..." I swallowed, breathing hard, "...you knew this whole time...?" but this threw him into an even madder fit of laughter which dyed my cheeks the hue of ripe cherries.

"*No!*" he gasped after noticing my face, slapping his hand against his folded knee, his eyes shut tight with tears dripping down his lashes, "Do you really think-..." he continued laughing, "Do you really think the Superiorii can actually," he breathed hard and continued laughing, "*read minds!*"

My teeth pinched my lip to not deny the question reflexively. He knew I thought the Superiorii could read minds and there was no point denying what he knew because it'd be pathetic, but I didn't want to admit my ignorance because then he'd think I was stupid. I was embarrassed over everything. So, I hastened to my defense, trying to save face.

"It's just..." I mumbled, "... I don't know what the Superiorii can or can't do! They're so mysterious and they keep everything so private and we're not allowed to know anything, so... so I don't know what you're capable of! So, stop *laughing* at me!"

"Jane, my darling, Jane," Superiorii Phorgiveness said after eradicating the smile from his face, "the Superiorii can't read minds. Whatever goes on in your mind is your secret. It's your world up there," he pointed a finger at my forehead and then gently pressed it against my furrowed brow, making the spot he touched radiate twinkling stars throughout my head and down my neck, "Don't allow your ignorance to foster fear towards the Superiorii. We're capable of doing the same things you are... the only difference between us and the rest of the congregation is we have influence."

"That's not..." I considered my choice of words, but realized I couldn't verbalize what is known as 'super powers'. The idea was there, but the words weren't.

"That's not what?" he encouraged.

"That's not... anything... I mean... that's not something that's too... how do you say it? I... If I wasn't a girl, I could do it too, but... it's something that everyone can do if given the role... I don't know how to explain myself- just forget it," I was talking way out of turn. Superiorii Phorgiveness was too intelligent not to notice, by my own indirect admission, I had too many thoughts looming within my mind.

"I know what you mean, Jane," he comforted, wrapping his arms around me, "it's not something a normal human being isn't capable of doing... right?"

I nodded and sank dizzied within his arms. His masculine energy, the bubble of protection, the feel of his stable arms, it was my cozy, firelit home in the middle of a brisk winter. All I needed was the smell of melting chocolate and apple spices to complete the mood.

"Despite that, it is power. It's something, though within the grasp of everyone, not everyone can do. They don't have the facility or capability of exerting influence like the Superiorii do."

"Why?" I lazily asked.

"Everyone has exalted us to a plane where we're infallible beings. Our word goes unquestioned out of fear or tradition. Even if our faults are clear to see, even monstrous, the congregation will ignore them out of submission. In that way, we can say whatever we please and everyone will register it as providential," Superiorii Phorgiveness must've known I couldn't understand half the words he was throwing out, but regardless he still expressed himself in his natural manner. As if he was speaking to a piece of himself.

"Superiorii Phorgiveness?" I called, trying to raise my eyes towards his, but only managing to gaze at his bearded jaw.

"Yes, Jane?" he answered.

"What does..." I was trying to recall the proper pronunciation

31

of the word, "...'en*light*en' mean?" but I overemphasized the 'light' part.

He looked down at me and began chuckling to himself. The idea that someone thought he could read minds must've given him a real kick.

"It means to give another person greater knowledge either in a particular subject, such as if I was to explain the Den Amfisvito to you, or in a situation. For example, explaining how the Superiorii cannot read minds and are capable of the same things everyone else is. Now," he leaned into me and stared into my eyes which made me feel like I was shrinking within his arms, "you have the same two options as before, Jane. Option number one is for me to share my opinion over your character. Option number two is for you to share your opinion over my character. Either way, both questions will be answered, but, once again, if you choose option number two, then you'll be... *enlightened*..."

I tried maintaining eye contact with him throughout his explanation, but after he flashed his heart stopping smirk at the word 'enlightened', my eyes cowered away and stared at a patch of bricks on the wall behind him. After learning that the word had nothing to do with light, I felt better about answering his question before he answered mine- especially if I was going to learn something from it.

"I'll answer your question first, Superiorii Phorgiveness," I blushed, trying to look at him again, but feeling my eyes slip away from his a second time. I breathed in, giving myself more time to think of a balanced, reserved answer, and exhaled sooner than I should've. Had I held my breath for as long as I needed to, though, I would've fainted. "I think... you're my friend," I started, hoping he couldn't hear my heart pounding, "I think you're someone I can tell anything to," which was a lie, but it's a lie I believed in, so a mistruth, "I also think you're intelligent. Very intelligent. And nice. You're nicer to me than my own parents..." I stopped speaking and flinched my gaze towards his. I went too far. I had insulted the honor of my parents, one of which was a member of the Superiorii, and his friend. I assumed even Superiorii Phorgiveness couldn't tolerate such disrespect, but he didn't say anything. His gaze didn't change. He was still listening to me.

"Go on," he encouraged.

I took another breath, sighed away my stress, and continued speaking, relieved I hadn't yet crossed a line with him, "You're the only person I feel comfortable around in the congregation. Everyone else has this sort of... I don't know," the word I was looking for was 'pretense', "it's like they're not really who they are. They're just pretending, but you're not pretending. You are the way you are and it's so nice to have someone like you in my life... If it wasn't for you... I'd feel..." The daydreams I'd have where I confessed my feelings to Superiorii Phorgiveness and have them reciprocated was a longshot away from reality. My hissing snake tongue, hastening to betray my secrets, was slowed by the alarm blaring away in my heart, slowing its pace until it froze clasped against the roof of my mouth like a prisoner. I was losing my modesty. He was a married man with a married daughter, many years older than me, and a grandchild. If he wasn't disturbed by my comment towards my parents, then he would at least be uncomfortable by a silly, little girl confessing her feelings towards him.

"... you'd feel alone?" he finished.

"Yes," I answered, still trying my best to look in his direction, but, instead, looking through the dark, empty expanse of our little room, "I'd feel horribly alone."

There was a silence between us. His hold on my arm grew looser and my heart wound up tighter with worry. Had I revealed too much? Was he disgusted by me now? I regretted and even hated him for pushing me towards confessing my opinion first. I asked him first! There was no need for all this nonsense! Besides that, where was this 'enlightenment' he was so keen on giving me? Had I missed my opportunity because I enlightened him on a matter he wasn't comfortable with? But my audacity! I was screaming at a member of the Superiorii! True, I was screaming at him in my head, but the Antifasi could still read minds. Even if the Superiorii couldn't, I knew the Antifasi was listening in on my insubordination.

"I'm sorry," I almost pled, feeling my chest crunch with heat, "I didn't mean to... I didn't... I was just trying to..." There were so many things I wanted to apologize for and I didn't know which one to pick just to finish my sentence. I didn't want the Antifasi to get mad at me for screaming at Superiorii Phorgiveness inside my head, but I was also afraid of telling Superiorii Phorgiveness about my screaming because it would make the situation even more uncomfortable. The guilt was racking my ribs like a xylophone, drumming them up and down, beating the confession out of me, chanting, 'Do you want to die? Admit to your sins. Do you want to die? Admit to your sins. Or you'll die.'

"Why are you sorry, Jane?" he asked. No one in the congregation ever asked me why I was sorry. They just half-heartedly accepted my random apologies and I appreciated that to a degree. I didn't like explaining myself- it embarrassed me, it felt like someone was sanding down an invisible bubble over my lungs. "There's nothing for you to be sorry over... you just expressed yourself... There's no shame in that, my dear. The only thing you should be sorry over is keeping your feelings all bottled up inside you."

"But..." I tried, "... I think of so many bad things... evil things... I'm scared..."

"Why?"

"Because I don't know what that means," I began shivering.

Superiorii Phorgiveness tightened his hold around me again, rocking me back and forth, with his hand supporting the back of my head like an infant's, my forehead resting against his collarbone. He was used to me shivering from time to time.

He knew what it meant better than I did. "The Fos Terata are not dwelling inside your mind, Jane," he assured, "you're a good girl... No matter what anyone says, you're a good girl- better than most."

"But the Fos Terata attack us through questions..." every word I uttered shocked my system into shivering even harder. "What if I'm a portal? What if that's the reason why Superiorii Faithfull keeps fighting father?"

"Is this what's been bothering you, Jane?" he asked.

I nodded and clenched my fingernails into his shirt, wadding up the fabric into a tight ball within my palm. "Yes..." I whimpered, "... are you going to tell on me now, Superiorii Phorgiveness?" I closed my eyes and held my breath for whatever was to come. I didn't want to face it, I wanted to run, I wanted to cry- the latter I did. There were tears dripping from the sides of my eyes, burning the pores within my cheeks.

"*Of course not*, Jane," he answered, passion in his tone, a pleasant surprise to me, he even held me tighter- maybe he did love me after all? His countenance soon calmed, though. Peaceful. "As you very well know, I've read the Den Amfisvito," he cleared the raw concern he previously had from his throat prior to restarting his explanation, "I've read the Den Amfisvito... I know what it says word for word because I've studied it my whole life. If I say there's no need for your grief, let alone *punishment*, then there's no need. Take my word for it. Trust me."

I wanted to, and my chest did clear up for a second after he said that, taking a gasp of cold air when it could, but I couldn't shake off my hot anxiety. His refusal to accept my blame and punish me only blazed my nerves like a summer's fire, worsened by the momentary clarity I felt, biting at me like a bitter example of what I'd never have. I hated myself. Why can't I be calm? Why can't I accept his kindness? Why do I have to torture myself? I would never know a permanent peace...

"But, the Superiorii have said time and time again that the

Fos Terata come through questions and people who constantly question are the Fos Terata's puppets, so how can there be no need for my grief? What if they take me? I don't want to be a portal, Superiorii Phorgiveness! I don't want to be a portal!" I exhaled, tensing up at all the information I'd carelessly revealed. I was exasperating him. He was going to get sick of me and leave.

"They won't take you, Jane," he assured in an even authoritative tone, "If I say there's no need, then there's no need. Take my word for it. Don't question me on this. If there's one thing you shouldn't question- it's this. Your questions, whatever they might concern, are allowed and you can think about them all you want. The Fos Terata won't get you. The Superiorii cannot read your mind. The Antifasi can't read your mind either. It's in the Den Amfisvito. Your mind is all your own and you're safe in there. Nothing and no one can invade it without your consent. Questions are not portals for the Fos Terata. Questions bring nothing more than more questions which is fine. That's how you learn. There's only one thing you need to be careful about and it's asking anyone within the congregation for answers... Remember this... If you want to ask anyone questions, ask only me, hopefully, I'll be able to answer them. If I can't, then we'll take it from there, talk about it, and try to find an answer together. Alright, Jane?"

I nodded my head again and did my best to stop shaking by focusing on my breath. I used a breathing technique Superiorii Phorgiveness taught me where I draw in long, deep breaths and make sure the exhale is longer than the inhale. He said if he wasn't around to help me through my shakes, then I should try focusing on my breath. He was there, though, brushing my arms, soothing the snapping nerves out of them, so it didn't take too long for me to settle down. I closed my eyes, felt the wind kiss my throat up and down, felt my chest ascend and descend like an ocean's ship among the waves, and saw little white dots blinking away behind my eyelids. I liked closing my eyes just so I could watch all the patterns and dots swirling and blinking away behind my eyes. My own little world.

"Superiorii Phorgiveness?" I called.

"Yes, Jane?"

"What did you want to… *enlighten* me with?" I asked, recalling the word from the lights twinkling behind my eyelids.

"Well," he began, "you said you consider me your friend, right?" I nodded, "and you said you trust me, right?" I nodded again, "But I think you're scared to tell me any of your thoughts because you fear I'm like the others," I quickly tried to explain myself, but he wouldn't have it, "I don't hold it against you Jane because I understand… I know you're scared, but I want to let you know you can trust me with anything. I'm not like your father… I'm not like anyone you know… You can trust me. I will never betray you… That's what I wanted to enlighten you on."

I knew he meant what he said, but I also didn't think he completely understood what he meant. I possessed a foul mind, warped to its foundation, forever cursed with the need for puzzling thoughts, so I didn't deserve his kindness. If he understood me, he would've needed to betray me to save himself from damnation. What if I was killing Superiorii Phorgiveness by association? I was a selfish cretin. I preferred to risk the life of the only person who showed care for me for the sake of not being alone. He could never understand me. Anyone who understood me, had to share my demented mind and Superiorii Phorgiveness possessed only beautiful thoughts. The one thing I wanted, understanding, and no one could give it to me. I was too complicated for even a man as intelligent as Superiorii Phorgiveness to understand- too malevolent for a man as well-intentioned as Superiorii Phorgiveness to help. I was doomed.

"Superiorii Phorgiveness?" I called, feeling my sides cringe from how many times I called out his name randomly throughout the night like a little girl calling out to her father.

"Yes, Jane?" he smiled.

"What do you think about my character?" The more genuine question, the question I wanted to ask, would've been- what am I to you? But I considered it far too grotesque to think about. It was fundamentally licentious, coming from a lustful place.

"I think," he paused, twisting his lips to the right side of his face, collecting all the right words he could within the time afforded, "and I stress the word *think* because only you know the real you. Everyone else just has their perception of you, but I think-..."

"What's perception?" I asked, quickly regretting not having let him finish his statement. I didn't care about the definition, I wanted his opinion.

"It's the way you see a thing...!" he answered, noticeably excited, "For example... that door across the room. Raise your thumb and compare it to the door," which I did, "Does your thumb look like it's the same size as that door?"

"Yes."

"Is your thumb the same size as that door?"

"No?"

"That's perception. The way you see the door right now is your perception of the door, but once you get closer to it, your perception of the door will change. However, the door is always going to remain the same."

"Unless it's smashed!" I smiled, delighted I thought of something witty to say.

"Unless it gets cut down or ripped apart or maybe burned..." Superiorii Phorgiveness smiled, "...the door is going to remain the same... You are always going to be you no matter what anyone else thinks of you. Including myself. What they think of you is their perception of you, but it's not the real you. However, to answer your question..." I looked up at him, snapping my gaze onto his face in fixed excitement, but he took another pause. He was keeping me on edge and I was about to sprint out of his arms in hysteria, "... I care about you, Jane..." he finally said, shooting my heart with merry adrenaline, "... you remind me a lot of myself when I was your age..." I was dying from joy, "I don't know what it's like to be the daughter of a Superiorii, but I know what it's like to be the son of one. And like you, I thought a lot, too. I was told the Fos Terata would get me if I questioned too much and I lived my boyhood in fear of being used as a portal, but it's just a scary story..."

I felt a buzzing, warm moment between us, whether it was real or imaginary, my heart told me it was the right time to tell him I loved him. Reach for a kiss, steal it from his lips, embrace him, sink away from the world in each other's arms, and fall away from reality by falling in love. I didn't have the nerve, though...

"So, the Fos Terata can't use people as portals?" I instead asked.

"No, Jane. It's not real... none of it-..." he paused, "They can't use you as a portal. You're safe within your mind and here with me."

I blushed and felt my cheeks screw into a knot from how big I was smiling. He liked me. Whether it was romantically or platonically, I didn't know and it didn't matter because he liked me. It should've been obvious, but I needed someone to remind me I meant something to them. My mind often reminded me how irksome my existence was, so to have positive validation was the best and rarest feeling in the world to me.

But now I had a new question buzzing through my mind...

"Superiorii Phorgiveness?" I called out once again.

"Yes, Jane?" he giggled, noticing the absurdity of my addressing him every couple of minutes when I was sitting in his arms in an empty room.

"If the Fos Terata can't use me as a portal... and if I'm in no danger from thinking whatever thoughts I have... and if the opinions of others over my character don't matter... then why can't I talk about my thoughts to others? It's not something worth feeling guilty over, right?"

"You shouldn't feel guilty about what you think, that's true," he quickly said, holding his breath, batting out every word hastily, as if the more time he spent answering, the deeper the idea of me telling others my opinions would simmer into my mind, "Every person here has their own world inside their mind. However, every person within the congregation seems to share the same world because it's easier. They let others get inside their head and they get inside the minds of others to make sure everyone's world looks exactly like theirs. They'll tell you how to think and what to do and how to feel and if you don't do what they say, they'll get you in trouble. Do you want to be like everyone else, Jane?"

"No," I somewhat lied. If being like everyone else meant I could feel understood and at peace, then I wanted to be like everyone else.

"Then it's best if you keep your thoughts to yourself... Otherwise, the congregation will get you into a lot of trouble for being different... especially if you don't change- which is impossible for people like us," that disheartened and hollowed me out, "No one here thinks like we do, but if we keep them from finding out about our thoughts, then they won't even know our worlds exist!" he beamed, "It'll be our own secret world!"

My very own private world with Superiorii Phorgiveness. What more did I need to smile from ear to ear? "It'll be our own secret world away from everyone else?" I blushed, but I had to look at him. I wanted to see him say yes with his eyes.

"Away from *absolutely* everyone," he promised, "and there'll be no more sermons, no more rules, no more potatoes," I laughed, "you can grow out your hair and brush off all that dirt from your face and eat good food and play and ask all the questions you want!"

"And you'll be there!"

"Answering any question you want to ask," he smiled.

"But what about what you want?" I asked, hoping he'd say me.

"Me?" he answered, laughing, "All I want is to get away from your father and Superiorii Faithfull's arguing."

C hapter Three

After my father closed the morning sermon, I stood beside him with my mother and James Virtew before the platform. We were listening to some mothers, accompanied by their little children, talk about how grateful they were for not being in the outside world. It was really two women speaking while the other three nodded in agreement, pacing their look between the two spokeswomen and my father for approval. Sister Gratefull, one of the two spokeswomen, after ranting against the outsiders, asked my father if there could possibly be one of them inside the congregation pretending to be one of us. Could they find our world and hide within it, leeching off our safety, to avoid being eaten by the Fos Terata? Of course, the answer was 'no'. We were all, biologically, family and the Antifasi would never allow an outsider to breech his sanctuary, but boredom can fuel paranoia, or hot gossip, so my father, not wanting to indulge her in either, answered, "Only the Antifasi knows."

"If one thing is certain, Sister Gratefull," said Sister Honestie, the second spokeswoman of the group, "the Antifasi knew they weren't good enough for our promised future. So, if one of them manages to sneak into our world, the Antifasi will kill them for us," she pursed her lips as if to say 'it's obvious' and continued, "Which reminds me," she turned towards us again, "I can't wait for the day the outsiders and Fos Terata are destroyed! We'll finally walk the Earth in natural light again!"

"Only one thing is certain?" Sister Gratefull mocked, sweeping a glance at my father, "Why, Sister Honestie! Everything is certain when it comes to the Antifasi! Be more careful with your words next time," she cautioned, "Or, who knows? You might find yourself being thrown in the furnace, too!" The other three women glared at Sister Honestie, looking at her like a stranger, a timbre in their eyes, but my mother, though cordial, was un-affected.

She was always so hollow, my mother. An echo incar-nated.

"I agree," a new voice interjected, footsteps drawing closer, and from my left, where my mother stood, Superiorii Phorgiveness took his place within our group, smiling, "For us to walk the Earth *again*," he corrected, "we would've needed to have al-ready walked the Earth before." Gradually, all five women were stunned- their eyes wide, bodies tight, and their audacities re-treating into their skin.

"Superiorii Phorgiveness!" My father smiled, welcoming him into his arms, "You're truly a wicked man!"

"Careful, Superiorii Loyaltie," he jeered, "If you speak too loudly, the congregation might throw me into the furnace!"

"Truly wicked!"

The five women watched the encounter in dumb silence with the group of three staring at their two former spokes-women. Sister Honestie was looking at the floor, an odd smile stitched onto her cheeks, a rag doll's empty smile. Sister Grate-full, though, was more confident. An unsteady, unfounded sort of defiance. Arrogance, really. "Superiorii Phorgiveness! Super-iorii Loyaltie!" she smiled, "What a privilege to be in the pres-ence of two wise Superiorii!"

"Three wise Superiorii," corrected a full, grounded voice thun-dering from behind the women.

Superiorii Faithfull, though domineering, was shorter than most women within the congregation. He walked with a limp in one leg and had a slight hunchback which was only no-ticeable if you looked at him from the right. His right ear was a shrivel of cartilage, a hole with some skin pressed around it, and his chin was sucked into his neck. Birth defects from inbreed-ing. It wasn't rare. No one noticed him approach us because the five women happened to be either his height or taller. However, upon his arrival, the five women excused themselves timidly and rapidly, like flustered grandmothers scattering away, with the arrogance of Sister Gratefull's eyes having flushed from her face immediately at the birth of his voice resonating behind her, and we were left alone with our little Napoleon.

"Superiorii Loyaltie," he addressed, his voice sounded off so deeply that I could feel it rivet through the stones beneath my feet, "We're going to speak."

"We've already spoken," my father retorted.

"Our conversations," Superiorii Faithfull countered, "have had no effect on how you conduct yourself on the platform... And out of love for you and your family, we're going to speak again."

"Superiorii Faithfull..." my father's eyes narrowed. I froze after hearing the severity in my father's tone. It was the ocean pulling in from the shore right before a crashing wave. He was trying to control himself, but I knew he couldn't. I flinched towards Superiorii Phorgiveness who stood unfazed by their tension. He was studying their interaction, analyzing them both. "You're a member of the Superiorii just like Superiorii Phorgiveness, Superiorii Depherence, and I. Do not pretend you're a higher authority and do not pretend you know more about the Den Amfisvito than we do. I will not now or ever preach your madness."

"You call the teachings of the Den Amfisvito madness, Superiorii Loyaltie?" Superiorii Faithfull's eyes managed to look both up and somehow down on my father.

"I never called the Den Amfisvito madness!" he defended.

"My teachings are from the Den Amfisvito, Superiorii Loyaltie," Superiorii Faithfull declared, "If there's a difference between what you say on the platform and what I command, it is only that I hold true to the Den Amfisvito's teachings regardless if they're considered severe. You prefer the congregation to live a peaceful existence at the expense of our promised future," he tisked at my father which made my father's complexion rouge, a string of veins pooling up from his temple like worms during a storm, "It's the responsibility of the Superiorii to correct one of their members when they become a little more... rebellious, Superiorii Loyaltie... Otherwise," his stare sharpened, "it's better for the congregation to throw themselves into the right furnace before that member drags them into the land of the Fos Terata with his false teachings."

"You're the rebellious one," my father hissed. His nostrils were flaring at each breath he exhaled, his chest pounding in and out.

"Isn't that what the outsiders told our ancestors when they were chosen for our sanctuary?" Superiorii Faithfull almost teased, "I'd be careful with your convictions, Superiorii Loyaltie... Arrogance never knows when it's wrong until the Antifasi shows it the answer... but by then it's too late to change your mind."

My father stood glaring at Superiorii Faithfull, his face as red as war, his nostrils beating the marching drum, and his eyes blaring the horn. Only his lips, as tight as his whitening fists, withheld the general tongue and its soldier words from battle. Superiorii Loyaltie, on the other hand, was steady. He had my father surrounded in his stare and was closing in. Had Superiorii Phorgiveness not informed me of the Superiorii's lack of mind reading, I would've suspected they were still arguing each other telepathically.

After a sigh sliced the tension, Superiorii Faithfull bowed his head, frowned, and looked back up at my father, "I don't hold any ill will towards you, Superiorii Loyaltie. In fact, quite the opposite, I respect both you and Superiorii Phorgiveness for your decency within the congregation... Unlike *others*..." he scowled, lowering his gaze to my father's chin, "...who *abuse* their title..." his eyes returned to my father's, along with his usual, strict composure and raised chin, "I just cannot abide by your sermons, Superiorii Loyaltie... You are leading the congregation down a path where righteousness and virtue are necessities too heavy to carry. We, as the Superiorii, must be the leaders of this congregation... not their friends or favorites..." he looked over at Superiorii Phorgiveness and then back at my father, "We need to show them the right direction with a firm hand pointing true."

"The Den Amfisvito never commanded the congregation to mutilate themselves," my father's eyebrow twitched with each consonant he clicked out.

"If you paid more attention to what you were reading rather than thoughtlessly flipping through the Den Amfisvito, accepting what others have told you about it since boyhood, then you would understand my point of view... It says to deaden the wants of the flesh and rid your mind of any impure thought. How else can someone deaden what naturally arises unless you cut your body of that impure nature entirely?"

"How would we distinguish the virtuous from the unvirtuous, then?" my father challenged, "If a person can commit an impurity, but chooses not to, then that person is virtuous at heart. But when you take away their choice, you can't tell who is or isn't virtuous anymore because they can't commit the action. The action is what helps us determine what's in the hearts of our brothers and sisters. How are we supposed to rid the congregation of the unvirtuous if we can no longer distinguish them?" It was his a-ha moment. It stole away some energy from Superiorii Faithfull's side of the conversation. He thought he stumped the stumpy man.

"Simple," Superiorii Faithfull answered, "We train the congregation to look for such treachery... If they suspect someone of acting, or even thinking, in discordance with what the Den Amfisvito commands, then the congregation must report that person to us and we will force them to show us their true nature in private."

Silence. My father disillusioned. We were trying to register the extent to which Superiorii Faithfull had thought out his plan. Did he already have an answer to everything?

"And how exactly do you plan on doing that?" asked my father, a petty jab of a question.

"It's fairly easy," Superiorii Faithfull assured, "With enough pressure you can get a confession out of anyone... With my tactic, catching people in the act or waiting for them to confess will no longer be necessary... We can make anyone suspected of an impurity confess by merely applying enough pressure for them to break."

"What sort of pressure?" my father interrogated, sloppily treading through the question like a drunkard with a purpose.

"Well, Superiorii Loyaltie," Superiorii Faithfull said, squaring out his posture, "with the pressure used by the Antifasi Himself."

I felt the group's energy tighten, so I looked over at Superiorii Phorgiveness, hoping he'd discreetly shed some clarity over what Superiorii Faithfull meant, a shift of the gaze, a purse of the lips, furrowing of the brows, anything, but I was told nothing. From the corner of my eye, I could see James standing incensed, looking very much like my father, while my mother, still holding her quiet countenance beside my father, had her eyes widened in disbelief. Superiorii Phorgiveness's eyes had narrowed. He was peering at the two men before us, watching them, closely. If I hadn't been so curious about what Superiorii Faithfull meant, I would've swooned over how handsome Superiorii Phorgiveness looked when focused.

"You mean throwing them in the furnace...?" My father's eyes were drowning beneath wrath.

"Of course not, Superiorii Loyaltie... How can we get a confession from the dead?"

"*Then say what you mean,*" he hissed through gritted teeth. His lips were starting to weaken behind the force of his tongue. He was losing his temper.

Superiorii Faithfull paused and examined my father. He glanced over at us, my mother and I, with pitying eyes and then back at him. "Careful, Superiorii Loyaltie..." he warned, "... don't become a slave to your emotions."

"At least I *have* emotions!" my father snarled, "How do you plan on forcing people to confess to acts they've only been accused of?"

"If they're being accused, then there must be a reason why," he answered, matter-of-factly.

"Out of scorned mouths come slanders looking for revenge."

"If the congregation lacks the morality necessary to know deceiving the Superiorii is punishable by death, then that's the fault of this laxed body of Superiorii," Superiorii Faithfull bashed both members of the Superiorii without effort. My father trembled with rage, but was unable to speak for the same reason. Superiorii Phorgiveness stood still like an island. He was separate from whatever storm was thundering and remained unaffected. "Besides," he continued, "the Antifasi is present when we make our decisions. He guides us down the righteous course... If someone is falsely accused, they should have nothing to fear. We would conclude their innocence soon enough and put their accuser on trial."

"*What are you talking about?*" my father snapped, "What 'trials'? The way we deal with matters now has worked since our ancestors were transported into this world! We throw people who we know have committed impurities into the furnace as it should be done with anyone who commits impurities! But that's only if we know for certain they have committed an impurity!"

"What about impurities of the heart, Superiorii Loyaltie?" Superiorii Faithfull rebutted, "No person can see what goes on inside the minds of our brothers and sisters, so how are we supposed to punish those who think impure thoughts? Thinking about committing the act is the same as committing the act... And we need to make sure the congregation is safe from those who think impure thoughts."

"That's for the Antifasi to decide! We cannot know what goes on within the minds of the congregation! Are you arrogant enough-...!"

"I will deal with everyone who has committed an impurity or has thought of an impurity the same way..." Superiorii Faith-full declared, stepping over my father's outburst, his insolence, with the ease of cracking twigs beneath his foot, "They will all be burned... and I will personally see to that justice."

My father's face dropped into perplexity. He looked like a delusional man confused as to where he was. My mother's face had hints of horror dotted across the corners of her stressed lips, her slightly widened eyes, the partially raised brow, as she held her own limp hands for comfort. James stared up at my father, waiting for him to react, but remained silently indignant and his defiance was stillborn. I looked up at Superiorii Phorgiveness again. I wanted to see his reaction to such a cruel and contradictory statement, but he didn't have one. He was still staring the at the two men, unchanged.

"You just said you couldn't get a confession from the dead!" My father finally contested.

"I'm glad my words aren't being wasted again," Superiorii Faith-full quipped, "I did say that... And my plan doesn't contradict that fact... I don't plan on burning the accused whole. I plan on burning parts of them. Their arms, their legs, their torsos with hot coals, but only if I'm feeling generous towards the accused. Otherwise, if the accused is clearly guilty and is only negating to postpone their execution, I'll set them on fire over and over again, putting out the fire every few seconds, so they can feel what's to come."

"That's monstrous..." my mother whimpered.

Superiorii Faithfull turned his attention towards my mother. He looked her in the eyes until she lowered her gaze and took the slightest refuge behind my father who wasn't offering any protection. My father's scowl pointed down towards a spot on the floor before my mother, caging my mother's figure within his peripheral vision. How dare a woman speak on matters between the Superiorii? Our being there was disrespectful enough, but the very fact that she would not only announce our presence, but go so far as to share her *opinion* was a humiliation. We were his spoiled children.

"Aunt Loyaltie-..." Superiorii Faithfull began.

"Superiorii Faithfull I beg you to ignore my wife. These matters aren't meant for the ears of women," my father demanded.

"Oh, but Superiorii Loyaltie," Superiorii Faithfull corrected, "these matters are indeed meant for the ears of women... and children. Everyone should hear the standards now expected of them and the punishment doled out for those who choose not to rise to those standards. That's what makes my plan so merciful... That's what I'm going to explain to your wife who, understandably, doesn't have the mind necessary to comprehend my plan," he embraced my mother in his gaze again. She was trying to further cower behind my father, but found no comfort in his presence, "Aunt Loyaltie..." his rough, baritone voice was sanded down to a smooth, mahogany tone. There was warmth emanating from him now. A genuine tenderness that I didn't think my mother had ever felt before, "I apologize if I wasn't speaking in plain enough terms... Frankly, I didn't think these matters would interest a woman of your fine character... or your daughter who I hold in the same regard..." he lowered his gaze towards me, smiled, and then brought it back up to my mother who was now looking him in the eye, but with a bowed head, "... I agree... If I didn't do my part in helping the congregation change to abide by the standards required of them, yet still punished them, it would be a monstrous plan. However, even before burning anyone, I would give them the chance to con-

THE LIGHT WAS GOOD

fess or explain themselves… Why would someone accuse them? Could they prove their innocence? If they could give me suffi-cient enough reason to believe in their innocence, then I'd set them free without a scar. It's when I know they're guilty that I'll burn them for a confession… I see the foundation of someone's character by looking at them… It's a gift from the Antifasi… If I can sense someone is a practitioner of impurities, I will torture them into admission. If I can sense someone is innocent, then all I'll need is an explanation."

"But they're just thoughts-…" my mother tried.

"*Joan!*" my father's voice slapped. His nostrils were flaring again and the veins in his neck were trying to grow as large as his pres-ence. He was still staring at the stone floor before her, but his stare seemed to encapsulate the room.

"It is fine, Superiorii Loyaltie…" Superiorii Faithfull insisted, using a voice that everyone present knew could roar far more powerfully than my father's, "… Yes, Aunt Loyaltie," he con-tinued, looking at my mother again who was now distancing herself away from my father, "They're just thoughts… but can you answer me this… How does the Fos Terata get inside our congregation?"

My mother glanced over at my fuming father, over-looked me, and then swept a pleading look to Superiorii Phor-giveness, "Through windows…?" she swallowed hard, seem-ingly anxious. She was a timid child between both men.

"Not quite…" Superiorii Faithfull's brows furrowed in concern, but when his eyes flashed back at my father and returned to my mother's presence, I knew his judgement was the least of her worries, "Do you want me to tell you?" he asked.

"Through questions…" she quickly answered inwardly, ignor-ing his help.

"Not just questions…" Superiorii Faithfull corrected, retaining his fatherly-like warmth towards my mother, "Our minds are the easiest way for the Fos Terata to invade our congregation... Any thought contradicting the Antifasi's wishes is a door for the Fos Terata to enter through. The more you think rebellious thoughts, the bigger the door gets. It's my job as a member of the Superiorii to make sure those doors aren't made. If they are, I must remove them from our congregation... Up until now, everyone has been taught only questions open doors for the Fos Terata... However, the Den Amfisvito mentions thoughts as doors as well... Do you think the Antifasi made us with thoughts, Aunt Loyaltie?"

She tried looking at Superiorii Faithfull from beneath her brows, but when her lips parted, her eyes instantly fluttered down, "No," she answered.

"Where do you think thoughts come from, then?" he asked.

"From the Fos Terata..." she answered, softly.

"Very good, Aunt Loyaltie," he congratulated.

"She's not a member of the Superiorii," my father interjected, "The people you need to convince of your madness are the Superiorii and I highly doubt any of us would appreciate you mutilating our wives, let alone our daughters, for the sake of your madness."

"You see it as mutilation, Superiorii Loyaltie, but it is their liberation. It is our liberation. We are freeing ourselves from carnal wants... I want to free this congregation from the depraved which linger among us... Do you think it's right for children to return to their families scratched, bleeding, or mute because a member of the congregation wouldn't restrain themselves?"

My father refused to answer.

"Do you think it's right, Superiorii Loyaltie?" Superiorii Faithfull's voice grew from his belly. There was deeper emotion sleeping there.

"No," my father answered.

"No," Superiorii Faithfull echoed, "Exactly... Then... how do you plan on stopping these men from hurting our children... our daughters... our sons...?"

"I don't have any sons..."

"Everyone within the congregation is our child, Superiorii Loyaltie," he corrected, glaring at him with more passion than my father could muster in his cowering presence. He wasn't scared of Superiorii Faithfull... but he was retreating within himself...

"But, the Den Amfisvito says-..." he tried.

"It says nothing... It was the first passage I looked for and it says nothing... Nothing at all... Nothing," Superiorii Faithfull huffed, wobbling a bit on his limp, "Yet, for some reason, our children are still suffering... We have been poisoned, Superiorii Loyaltie... Poisoned by the Fos Terata!" his stable foot stomped and he regained his composure, "And I intend to suck the poison out and spit it in the faces of those who have allowed the Fos Terata to enter our congregation... No matter what."

Superiorii Faithfull glowered at my father as all the bulging rage my father's eyes once had trickled into chagrin. Why was my father suddenly humiliated?

"Basically..." my father finally said, measuring out his words, "... the changes you want to implement include... genital... *sacrifices*... paranoia within the congregation... and persecution of those suspected of impurities and thoughts?"

Superiorii Faithfull didn't confirm. He was still glowering at my father until whatever sentiment he had boiling beneath calmed and receded back into the inner folds of his usual domineering temperament.

"You have your father's chin, Superiorii Loyaltie," Superiorii Faithfull observed.

"Is there anything else?" my father pressed, shaking off his observation.

"Yes..." Superiorii Faithfull answered, "... I want to persecute those who grossly abused the supposed alternative..."

"So, you want to persecute Superiorii Depherence?"

"I want to persecute anyone who grossly abused the alternative."

"Superiorii Depherence is a member of the Superiorii. He descended, like us, from the original Superiorii. You can't persecute him without just cause and your interpretation of the Den Amfisvito isn't just cause."

"Once the Den Amfisvito's true message becomes law, it will give me the just cause necessary to burn any man who has abused children even during a time when it was considered pure. However, as far as interpretations go, I assure you that my so-called interpretation will prove to be the most accurate account of the Den Amfisvito you and our congregation will live by," he drew a step closer to my father and said, "We will finally live in the purity expected of us by the Antifasi... We can rest assured that our promised futures are well within our grasp... Why can't you see the peace I will bring?"

My father took a step away from him, "Is that what this is really about?" he challenged, "Or are you trying to push your madness onto the congregation out of boyhood revenge, Julius...?"

Superiorii Faithfull's lower eyelids dripped with bitter nostalgia, a twinkle of tragedy spotting through his pupils, all engendered by my father's single remark, but our little Napoleon quickly drew in his clouds of composure to hide the lightning in his eyes, "No, Superiorii Loyaltie..." he answered, taking a step back from my father, "... I'm trying to cleanse the congregation of the madness already rampant... I will eliminate what you consider sanity... and we will live in a pure world which you consider 'madness'."

There didn't seem a need to say anything more. Superiorii Faithfull could've left and there would've been no questions left to ask. We understood his plan, his determination, and why he was so adamant upon seeing it succeed- at least, I thought I did. Still, though, we remained standing in our spots, looking at the same people we had been staring at the entire conversation. Superiorii Faithfull and my father didn't break eye contact. Neither of them bowed their heads or looked away. James was cutting his stare back and forth between both men, waiting, and my mother was gazing at the stone floor. She was probably tired from looking up beneath the weight of her brows. Superiorii Phorgiveness continued examining both men without adding even a breath to their conversation. What had he seen in their exchange?

"Jane!" a girl around my age called. Her name was Janice Orderlie II. She was a little older than me, but already married to a member of the congregation in his early thirties. Her husband was a widower whose first wife died from a miscarriage. His first wife was a petite, pubescent girl unready for labor. His dead wife's parents were still young enough to have another child, so they had Janice to replace their first daughter, his first wife, Janice. Janice Orderlie II bowed her head towards Superiorii Phorgiveness, James, my mother, my father, Superiorii Faithfull, and then addressed me again, "Jane! I need to talk to you about something..."

"What is it?" I asked.

"Do not be impolite, Jane," my father ordered, "Attend to Sister Orderlie."

Chapter Four

"I'm sorry for being rude, Janice..." I apologized.

I didn't want to create this awkward space between us where I lowered myself and expected her to pull me up through forgiveness, but I felt the need to apologize. Anxiety was vacuuming my chest airtight, my lungs bundling up my heart, and the only way to pop its hold was by apologizing. I risked choking if I took too long.

"It's okay," she smiled, "The conversation seemed interesting."

Janice was a sweet girl. She didn't act holier by demonizing others. She was a simple girl following the rules our world taught her to obey. It was comfortable being in her presence, but I knew she wasn't someone I could confide in. She had a limited mind. She would've grown up to be a kind woman, though.

"Did you overhear our conversation?" I asked.

"Not much... I think the brothers closer to your family overheard, but they probably didn't understand."

"What did you hear?"

"Something about protecting the children of the congregation," she answered, "and I agree with Superiorii Faithfull."

I was momentarily stunned by her forwardness. No one ever discussed personal views. It was dangerous, yet when it came to Superiorii Faithfull's reforms, it was tolerated? I wanted to state my viewpoint too, but it wasn't based on the Den Amfisvito or Superiorii teachings. Janice was agreeing with Superiorii Faithfull, but I wasn't agreeing with anyone. I was proposing my own ideas.

"I think everyone does," I answered, ignorantly, straddling the fence, wanting to blend into both common thoughts, "but there's a passage in the Den Amfisvito that allows alternatives..."

"Didn't Superiorii Faithfull say there isn't?"

"Yes... I mean... I don't want to question my father, but Superiorii Faithfull seemed quite adamant on the matter..." Was I being too aggressive? Flippant? Why did I state such a strong opinion in the first place? I never read the book! I'm such an arrogant fool.

"You sound like you agree with your father's teaching, Jane," she assured, "Superiorii Faithfull is the one questioning your father."

Guilt chafed my lungs. First, my mother speaks out of turn, then I comment my uncertainty over my own father's teachings. The shame was painful, but the dishonor felt lethal. If Superiorii Faithfull gained the congregation's favor, then nothing stopped him from persecuting my father, even my family, for the sake of atoning whatever hatred he had buried. What if I was aiding the rise of a dictator by remaining flippant? What if I was throwing myself on death's row for broadcasting my thoughts? I was getting ahead of myself. Superiorii Phorgiveness told me I worried too much and needed to let things go. Things weren't as grave as they seemed, but still... He also told me to be very careful for a reason.

"My father is a great teacher and a reliable member of the Superiorii," I corrected, "If Superiorii Faithfull wants to question him, then it's his decision, but that doesn't mean he is right in doing so no matter how strong his convictions are."

"There has to be a valid reason for him to question his own brother, Jane..." contested a shrill voice standing before us. Her voice wasn't overbearing, but after enough time listening to it, it pressed thorns against your ears.

Jeanette emerged from a crowd of four girls and approached me with open arms, embracing me. I rubbed her shoulder as a sign of reciprocation, but tightened my muscles to shorten the hug. She smelled of sharp sweat, like most people in the congregation, but there was something else which made her scent unbearable. I couldn't identify it at the time because I hadn't been around anything like that smell before. Rotten fish was never on the congregation's menu. It wasn't until I was in the outside world, passing a local fish market, that I figured out the stench.

After slicing off her clitoris and labia, Jeanette's vagina grew gangrenous.

Despite that, her collected friends didn't abandon her. They remained by her side like dogs on short leashes. Though, I'm sure even a dog would've tugged away desperately from the evil lurking between Jeanette's thighs. Jeanette was magnetic regardless of how she smelled. She was charismatic, charming, and confident, capable of swaying minds with relative ease. She was the stone these girls clung onto for air in this flooded world. That made her character more dangerous than her stench.

"... I understand you respect your father. He's a very respectable man and we all respect him, too," she turned towards her nodding followers for confirmation, pleased with their robotic agreement, and looked back at me. She had the same authoritarian stare her father-in-law did. I tried my best to maintain eye contact, but couldn't help skipping my eyes over the floors, towards the walls, and at Jeanette's chin. "He's a man worth respecting because he works hard as a member of the Superiorii, along with Superiorii Phorgiveness, and he's never abused a child..."

I contemplated Jeanette's impression of my father and wanted to contradict her. Inform her of how she was wrong, but it would've been disrespectful towards him. Yet, if I agreed with her, wouldn't I be lying? It felt like a trap, a poisoned double-edged sword waiting to slice into my flesh and corrode my insides with its venomous guilt. "I have to excuse myself, Jeanette. Janice and I need to talk about something," I tried.

"Oh, no!" Janice corrected, "Jeanette was the one who wanted to talk to you. I'm sorry if I forgot to tell you."

"Oh…" my stomach swelled. My only chance to escape and it was easily dashed. I was chained to them. The key to my freedom lied in the palm of Jeanette's hand.

"Your wanting to attend to those who express a need to confide in you is admirable, Jane," Jeanette complimented, "It shows you have genuine consideration for the wants and needs of others. You'll make a great wife to a Superiorii one day."

"Thank you," I said. The flattery felt dishonest. She was trying to trade goods in return for a service. "What can I help you with, Jeanette?"

"I was hoping to help *you*, Jane!" Her voice curved up higher by the last word as if squeezing out the desired sentiment and she then grabbed my hands without intent of letting go. She was trying too hard. You never know what to expect from people who try clawing their nails into you. What lengths they'll take to possess your time. "I thought it best to pull you out of the Superiorii's discussion. Women shouldn't listen to their affairs. It'll hurt their minds… Make them think… inappropriate thoughts," she turned towards her followers, nodding to them which they mimicked in return, all of them looking at me. "I'm afraid I couldn't help your mother very much, but I'm sure Aunt Faithfull is already sending one of our older sisters to pull her away as well."

"Their conversation was heated at first, but by the time I left, things had cooled down," I informed, "Thank you nonetheless, but was there something you wanted to talk about?"

"Very direct, Jane," she straightened her posture, looked back towards the others, and then pursed her lips. Was she making fun of me? "I appreciate that. Not only do you have a genuine character, but an efficient one, too."

"Thank you," I repeated. My gratitude was feigned and hollow, but I still had to remain respectful for appearance. Maybe I wasn't so genuine after all.

"But yes," she nodded, her strong pupils, pushing against mine, throwing mine to the ground, locked onto my eyes, "I needed to talk to you about matters concerning the congregation. We are the future wives to the future Superiorii. Though we'll leave the laws to our husbands, it's going to be our responsibility to enforce them."

I reserved my response because I felt unsafe. I couldn't understand why I felt unsafe, but Superiorii Phorgiveness advised me to be cautious. For the rest of our conversation, I calculated my responses the same way I thought Superiorii Phorgiveness would if he was in my place. I pretended I was Superiorii Phorgiveness studying Superiorii Faithfull instead of Jane intimidated by Jeanette. "That's an interesting way to look at our positions, Jeanette," I smiled, "and it's also something I haven't heard before. How did you come to this conclusion?"

"It's something I learned from Superiorii Faithfull," she answered, proudly beaming, "He's been guiding our family down a path that, in truth, seems more fitting for the righteous. There's reason behind every direction he gives us and, though we should obey him for the sake of obedience, he explains his guidance, so we understand why we must inculcate his lessons into ourselves and others with zeal. Do you know why the wives of the Superiorii should be the ones enforcing the laws instead of the responsibility resting solely with the Superiorii, Jane?"

"No," I answered.

I tried predicting her response before she said it like Superiorii Phorgiveness did with me the night before. I predicted she would say something along the lines of, 'The Superiorii are busy studying the Den Amfisvito and attending to other responsibilities, so they don't have the time necessary to focus entirely on the congregation. With the laws my father-in-law has in mind, we need to observe the congregation for ourselves and see who lacks a virtuous heart. The weight of that responsibility should weigh heaviest upon the Superiorii's wives' shoulders since we can report those we suspect to the Superiorii directly.'

My prediction was correct. I tried suppressing the smile forcing its way across my face as she spoke, but I had to cover my mouth until it was my turn to speak again.

"But…" I thought, trying to compose my argument, "if someone is guilty of an impurity… they should confess or be caught in the act… There's never been a need for such… attentiveness among us… Don't you think that might cause…" I was trying to recall the word my father used with Superiorii Faithfull, "… paranoia? What if someone accused someone else falsely out of revenge?" It was an innocent inquiry. There was no passion behind my challenge unlike my father's. This was a debate on hypotheticals. Nothing serious. However, I still felt the blood boil beneath my face, rouging it, because I was asking for and receiving too much attention.

"Our congregation's purity is already tainted by certain practices. Once we slice impurities from our flesh, we can discuss distinguishing the virtuous from the unvirtuous. It'll be difficult to see who serves the Fos Terata once actions can't reveal them, so we must look towards certain…" she thought, "…indications… of a man's virtue…"

I was going to say the term she was looking for was 'character clues', but it felt like a secret term only Superiorii Phorgiveness and I knew about. And I wanted to keep it that way. I locked my hand over my mouth again to jail myself from reflexively saying something I might later, or immediately, come to regret and continued looking her in the eye. She wasn't done answering me.

"... as for paranoia and false accusations, rest assured Superiorii Faithfull has an excellent eye for spotting the virtuous and those lacking. If someone is accused falsely, he will note their innocence and burn the accuser."

When she finished, I looked at her unresponsive for a second more. I wanted to study her like Superiorii Phorgiveness had studied Superiorii Faithfull. My silence seemed to threaten her, though, because her stare turned defensive.

"Do you have an opinion of your own on this matter, Jane?" she asked, smiling soon after.

"No," I quickly answered. I didn't expect her to question me and the countenance she took on, one of intimidation seasoned with forced kindness, unnerved me. Despite that, I immediately hoped I hadn't given away any of my character clues.

"So, you're in agreement?" she asked.

Agreement? It wasn't that simple. I agreed child abuse needed to be eradicated and the abusers burned, but I did not agree with genital mutilation. I did not agree with burning people for confessions. Jeanette's question was black and white. I had to answer either 'black' or 'white', yes or no, to not draw attention towards myself. I had to show everyone nothing, so they wouldn't suspect a capability of critical thought in me, but I wanted to be genuine. I wanted to splash color over this bland canvas and give my nuanced opinion regardless of what the Den Amfisvito said.

'What would Superiorii Phorgiveness do? What would Superiorii Phorgiveness do?' The question looped itself in my mind, begging for a clear answer. It was counter-productive, though. This constant line of questioning took up too much headspace, so I couldn't tactfully think about anything else. I was getting flustered.

"Jane?" she called, looking at me with a feigned sense of concern.

"I..." I tried, "... I see where you're coming from. Superiorii

Faithfull has thought his reforms through... but there's a couple points I don't agree with."

I should've just left it at 'Superiorii Faithfull has thought his reforms through' without adding a 'but', but that's my pestering nature. I wanted to be genuine and hoped others would understand my honest opinion. They didn't. They never do.

"And... what don't you agree with?" Jeanette asked.

She crossed her arms in indignation and further straightened her posture. A habit I'm sure she developed from Superiorii Faithfull. She kept a smile secure across her face, but her eyes revealed her true feelings. Why wasn't I making this easy for her? Why couldn't I agree? What was the matter with me? Her judging, blue eyes sheltered beneath her furrowed brows flung my eyes around the room. I was too weak to handle my contrary position. 'I'm wrong, I'm wrong, I don't know anything, I'm wrong!' I was expected to answer for an opinion I couldn't explain...

"I'd rather go back to my parents now," I answered, noting my parents still standing with Superiorii Phorgiveness.

"What...? No, Jane," she whipped her head shocked someone could be so ridiculous and strengthened her stare against me. It was belittling. I could feel my head physically being lowered by her stare, "Tell me what you don't agree with," she demanded.

'She's going to scream at you. She's going to scream at you. She's going to embarrass you. What would Superiorii Phorgiveness do? What would Superiorii Phorgiveness do?'

"I don't want to say, Jeanette..." I could barely speak her name. I was so nervous about further disrespecting her, stating her name through my foul lips felt like a slap to her face.

"Do you disagree with Superiorii Faithfull trying to rid the congregation of child abusers? Protecting children like Judith here who is being abused nightly by Superiorii Depherence?" She turned towards Judith, one of her followers, who I hadn't noticed before. When I crawled my gaze across the floor and flicked it quickly up towards her, I noticed her bruised eye, swollen, with red specks splattered on a blue canvas, scratches, bite marks, and faded scars on her cheeks. Who knows what else in other places...

"No, of course not..." I protested, gutted by how easily victims were overlooked, but Jeanette was heated.

"Then what? His passion to lead the congregation down a righteous path? The hard work we need to put forth to keep this congregation safe?"

"No!" but it *was* that. It's the way she worded herself which made me reflexively say no as if I'd be a monster to say yes. I didn't agree with the 'hard work'. The hard work meant genital mutilation, paranoia, and if that's the answer, then aren't we replacing one trauma with another?

"Then what is it, Jane?" she demanded.

"I don't know," I answered.

"You don't know?" she puzzled, looking at the ceiling for an answer to my stupidity as if it was etched onto its stone and then towards her followers in disbelief, "Well, neither do I Jane, so why don't you tell me what you don't agree with and I'll explain it to you until you understand."

"I understand it now," I tried, "There's no need for explanation. Thank you, Jeanette," I was almost begging her to stop. My body needed her to forget the subject and let me go, but she wouldn't give me the satisfaction. She was too 'strong-willed'.

Jeanette paused and returned to her onslaught, "What do you understand now, Jane? Are you saying you understand Superiorii Faithfull's reforms and still don't agree with him? Or have you changed your mind and now agree with him?"

"Be clearer, Jane!" One of her followers complained.

Tarantulas birthed from my organs, splintering their

hairy legs over them, conquering them, and before I knew it, I was shaking. I did my best to force my muscles into place, but they wouldn't comply. I imagined Superiorii Phorgiveness holding me, brushing my nerves into place, but that didn't work either. There were loud voices. The girls were staring. They were waiting.

"I understand his decision," my throat dried. I pushed my clammy tongue through its fits, but my throat sometimes swallowed itself up. When that happened, I couldn't speak no matter how hard I concentrated through the nerves. I hadn't reached that point yet, but I felt it coming.

"Do you agree with him, Jane?"

Jeanette was incessant. I was once again faced with choosing between expressing my genuine opinion or answering falsely. I wouldn't need to explain myself if I chose the latter because she would give herself that explanation. In her mind, it was clear why anyone would side with Superiorii Faithfull. But... an even graver thought than having to explain myself occurred to me.

They were going to intimidate me into saying yes. Superiorii Faithfull intimidated my father into silence. Who knows what Aunt Faithfull had in mind for my mother if she pulled her away from my father's company like Jeanette said she would? All they needed was enough pressure to push everyone to their side and once that happened, their rules would take effect. The congregation would go down Superiorii Faithfull's 'righteous' path. I felt the need to say no and rebel against their plan. I was not going to help their reality take fruition. I was going to state my genuine opinion and explain it openly...

... at least, that's what I wanted to do.

Superiorii Phorgiveness warned me against speaking my mind. I could only talk about my thoughts with him, but I had to reserve myself with everyone else. Why? I only knew if I gave enough character clues to reveal my independent thoughts, I'd get into some, possibly lethal, trouble. However, I was disagreeing with something most people already disagreed with. If anything, Superiorii Faithfull, his family, and their followers were the ones thinking for themselves. I didn't want to argue with Superiorii Phorgiveness, though. Not even in my head. I trusted his judgement. If he didn't want me to do something, then I was going to listen to him... like I was expected to listen to James one day.

"I can understand where Superiorii Faithfull is coming from," I tried, still forcing out the words through the swelling in my throat, "and I think it's very noble of him to want to correct the..." I wanted to say abuse, but in case I was speaking against the Den Amfisvito, I said, "... way men use children within the congregation."

"What about his new set of expectations? His mode of discipline? Do you agree with those as well?" Jeanette insisted.

I almost moaned in frustration. 'No! I don't agree with that! What sort of barbarian burns people for confessions? The idea itself is not only horrible, but stupid! People will confess to anything if they're tortured into doing so! It doesn't take the Antifasi to know that hence why he doesn't demand burning people for confessions! He expects them to confess from their own free will! Then we burn them alive as punishment for the impurity they either confessed to or were caught committing! And even then! Why do they have to be burne-...' I stopped myself. I was a step too close to questioning the Antifasi again. I didn't have the audacity to say all of that. Jeanette would've burned me herself.

My shivering got worse with my frustration. I held myself tightly and tried imagining Superiorii Phorgiveness standing behind me, holding me, helping me. 'Please help me...' I thought, melting out the sound banging around my head, 'Please help me.' I focused on a couple stones nestled in the floor on Jeanette's left until her presence vanished. I focused on my breathing, on the beats within my head, and tried calming my body down.

Breathe in...

... breathe out.

Breathe in...

... breathe out.

Breathe in...

... breathe out.

Breathe in...

... breathe out.

Breathe in...

... breathe-...

"Jane!" Jeanette ordered, "Do you agree with Superiorii Faithfull's expectations and his discipline!"

I whimpered at the shock of hearing such a shrill voice shatter my concentration. I was so close to calming my body down...

"Jeanette!" I cried. I was going to tell her exactly what I thought of Superiorii Faithfull's rules and where she could shove his ideas and what else she could cut off and who they can throw into the furnace first, but before I did, my meditation rendered providence.

"Jane?" a tender voice called from behind me. It was strong, warm, and comforting. My home. Despite Superiorii Phorgiveness claiming the Superiorii couldn't read minds, I knew he could at least hear my heart. "Your parents asked me to tell you they're going back to their quarters and wish you to join them."

"Of course," I nodded, still shaking. I turned towards Jeanette, Janice, Judith, the other three girls, and excused myself, walking away with my beloved Superiorii Phorgiveness's protection.

"Bullies, the lot of them, little, broken monsters, what happened, Jane?" he asked.

"They kept asking me if I agreed with Superiorii Faithfull... and I tried answering in a way I imagined you would... but I couldn't... I'm not smart like you."

He looked at me with tragedy in his eyes. Hurt by what I had said. I looked up at him, wanting him to hold me. I wanted him to make my nerves stop snapping.

"We'll talk about this later, Jane..." he assured, "... but right now your parents want you."

"Why?" I asked.

"I don't know, but try to watch what you say when you're with them..." he cautioned, "... I can tell your father is... not calm..."

"Oh..." I shrugged, still holding myself, shaking harder, my heart sinking lower.

Superiorii Phorgiveness brushed his hand against my arm, discreetly, the one facing away from the congregation. When I noticed him smiling down at me, I felt better. My arm stopped shaking and soon after my entire body calmed down.

"Are you going to walk me to my family, Superiorii Phorgiveness?" I asked.

"I'll be with you every step of the way," he promised.

THE LIGHT WAS GOOD

Chapter Five

Our room was the same size as every other room in the underground. There was one small bed married couples slept in, smaller than your world's equivalent of a full bed, in each room. In our case and many others, however, my father was the only person who slept in the family bed. He demanded the bed because he was the head of our household and he was given it without question. I didn't very much mind it. My mother slept on the floor and I slept in an empty room with Superiorii Phorgiveness.

The Superiorii and their families slept in the right hallway, by the entry, where the Den Amfisvito was kept. Our rooms were closest to the right furnace. The people burned there were dead. Gone. I never liked going down the left hallway because the same wasn't true for its furnace. The punished lived in anguish there. They were brutalized in eternal torment for their crimes against the congregation. They hated us, especially the Superiorii who sent them there, so I could only imagine what they would do to one of their daughters. I was scared if I passed by their room, or dared to look in, I'd be grabbed by the punished and dragged into the land of the Fos Terata.

"*'That's so monstrous!' 'But they're just thoughts!'*" My father mocked. I could hear him squealing through the door. I didn't want Superiorii Phorgiveness to leave me there with them. I wanted him to carry me off where we could imagine another world together.

"Superiorii Phorgiveness...?" The shivers were returning. My nerves snapping in my upper arms. The muscles in my throat were contracting at a pattern which couldn't facilitate speech.

He was looking at me before I looked at him, knowing

what he had to do and lamenting it. He wasn't looking at me with sympathy like a bystander watching police take away victims of a crash. It was deeper. Empathy. He understood.

I called his name hoping he would read my heart again and take me away, but this case was different. He couldn't be my savior. He had to leave me alone in that small room flooded with my father's large rage. The good thing is I no longer drowned beneath his emotions. I learned how to swim, clinging onto lifesaving dreams, but I wasn't an expert, yet. There were times when I was sucked into the undertow of my father's turbulence and when that happened... I wanted to drown. I preferred it over the struggle.

Superiorii Phorgiveness turned towards the entry of the hallway, one door down, and looked over the crowd, checking if the coast was clear. It was.

He knelt before me, wrapped his arms around my shoulders, and pulled me in. Holding my head against his neck like a father holding his newborn infant's soft head, his entire hand enveloping the back of my skull. His hugs were as tender as his voice, as warm as his gaze, and as comforting as... being hugged by someone who never made you feel misplaced. I didn't hug him back. My arms were too numb and my body shook harder and harder, but he soon soothed me. He melted one hand into my back and flowed the other into my arm. "We'll be together tonight, Jane..." he comforted, "... and then we'll laugh and forget."

"Okay..." I mumbled into his skin. When I turned my face towards his neck, not wanting to drool on his shirt, he pulled away. It disheartened me because I wanted to feel my lips on his neck, smell his person, take in his sensitivity. His jaw, hanging above, had sheltered my head, nestling it beneath him, but now I felt the freezing hot flashes of embarrassment. Had I given my feelings away? Was he uncomfortable with me now? My paranoia devoured every comfort he had given me and pulverized it.

He stood up, leaving me cold. When he opened the door, I was frozen. By the time I walked in, by the time he closed the door behind me, I was ice.

"What took *you* so long?" my father interrogated.

"Jeanette wouldn't stop asking me about Superiorii Faithfull's reforms," I answered. I was a machine rattling out coherent sounds rather than a little girl talking with her father, but it was difficult to keep up an appearance. My mind was too busy thinking about whether Superiorii Phorgiveness was uncomfortable with me or not than trying to be respectful.

"Oh! So, now *she* thinks she's a Superiorii!" he screamed, circling in place, throwing his arms up as if he was holding air, "This entire congregation is going to spiral into chaos and then who'll be there to help us? Superiorii Faithfull? Mark my words," he snapped his finger at my mother, pointing at her in the back-left corner of the room, her eyes closed, a frozen calm about her body, not even breathing. He leaned in her direction while looking at me with his manic eyes, "if Superiorii Faithfull manages to corrupt this congregation, we will throw ourselves into the right furnace together... It's better to die serving the Antifasi than to live beneath the tyranny of a madman. They'll all be thrown into the land of the Fos Terata... him and all his followers!"

"If he's leading the congregation to the Fos Terata, then why doesn't the Superiorii remove him from power?" I asked.

"*Because, Jane!*" he barked, mocking me as if I should've already known the answer, "If he's removed from power, then people will question. If people question, then the Fos Terata will get in. If the Fos Terata get in, then the congregation will blame the Superiorii. If there's an entire congregation of people angry at a few, even if they are the Superiorii, you can't predict how they'll react, but it will not end well for the few involved. Then, Superiorii Faithfull will get the power he wants and claim the congregation for his own until three new members are found, if he lets them be found, and only the Antifasi would know what to do then... That's why, Jane! You cannot remove a member of the Superiorii without the congregation questioning the decision!"

By the time he finished, he was leaning in my direction, pointing at me, his stare grabbing my head and lowering it like a dog smelling its own feces. I feared looking at him, let alone in the eye, but I still had questions. I wanted to help. I wanted to propose reconciliations to his problem and give him peace of mind. Whether it was to help or analyze a problem, solve it, and prove I wasn't stupid, I wanted to contribute. It was another facet of my personality that was difficult to keep under wraps. "What if..." I started, but my lips quickly stitched themselves shut as if my body knew better than my mind.

"What if..." he shook his head, his eyes widening, waiting impatiently, "*What*, Jane?!"

"What if..." I mumbled through my sealed lips, "... what if you and Superiorii Faithfull found common ground...? Don't you think it would be...?"

"*'What if you and Superiorii Faithfull found common ground?'*" he mocked, taking up a tone that was far higher and shriller than my voice actually was, "I do think, Jane. I think a lot unlike you and your mother, so save your little suggestions for Jeanette!" he laughed and then turned towards my mother again, "Isn't that great? Both my wife and daughter are against me!"

"No, I'm not, John," my mother tried.

"*Woman!*" my father roared, "*You've humiliated me enough!*"

Whenever my father lost control over his emotions, which was often, he would blame either my mother or I even over matters which didn't concern us. He would say it was our fault for not helping the situation or not doing enough or not being better or not being present or whatever else he could think of. His accusations and expectations reached heights which would mean suicide if someone fell from them. I took his demands to heart when I was little, but by that point in my life, I accepted I would never be good enough. I tried so hard to make him happy, but it was never enough. The worst part is I didn't realize his expectations were unrealistic until later.

"I'm sorry, John!" she cried, *"I didn't mean to speak out of turn!"*

"Maybe I can work something out with Superiorii Faithfull," he swiped a glance at me to further mock my idea, "where women cut their tongues out, too... I'm sure the two of you wouldn't mind considering how you're perfectly alright with mutilating yourselves anyways."

"I'm not okay with that, father," I corrected, but I immediately regretted speaking again. Cutting my tongue out might not be such a bad idea after all?

If stares were fire, I would've been ash beneath his glare. His body shook like a soldier conquering a battlefield, his nostrils flared, and what was left of his teeth was clearly visible, his lower jaw pushing beyond his upper teeth. I retreated into a corner, the one made by the door and adjacent wall, but my father charged towards me. *"YOU WILL RESPECT ME!"* he screamed. Before he struck me, he swung at the door I was standing against and bashed his fist against it over and over again. *"YOU WILL RESPECT ME! YOU WILL RESPECT ME! YOU WILL RESPECT ME!"* The doors in the underground were made from thick, solid wood, so there was more damage done to his bleeding knuckles than to the door itself, but I could still feel the door rivet behind me, hurting my spine. He didn't hit it once. He hit it three times. After every scream, he crushed his bones against the wood the way he wanted to hit me. He never laid a finger on me, but sometimes I wondered... Was the fear worse than the physical pain he would inflict?

"Does this family even know what respect means!" he exhaled, whipping away from me and towards my mother, "Maybe if you were a better mother, your daughter would've been raised with

ANGELICA LABYRINTH

decency instead of pride!"

As he continued berating my mother and my mother continued sitting there, crying, begging his forgiveness, drawing him closer to her, I imagined Superiorii Phorgiveness. He was standing behind me, holding me, soothing me, relaxing me, and assuring me he would always be with me regardless. He was watching my father scream at my mother and promised he would never scream at me like that. He would never even raise his tone against me. He would take care of me, protect me, and when we were married, treat our child with the same tenderness.

"But why can't you and Superiorii Faithfull work towards common ground, John?" my mother supplicated, "No one wants their children to be alternatives!"

"Open your legs, Joan!" he demanded, "Let me save you the trouble Jeanette had to go through and mutilate you myself!"

'What do you think about all this, Superiorii Phorgiveness?' I asked my imaginary friend.

'I think it's monstrous, Jane,' he answered.

'I'm not talking about my father's threats, Superiorii Phorgiveness. I'm talking about my father's, and I think the congregation's, opinion on common ground. It seems like a good idea to me, but what do you think? Is there something I don't understand because it seems everyone thinks it's a terrible idea?'

'I don't know... ask me tonight, Jane.'

"*Jane!*" my father commanded, "Go bring some scissors from Superiorii Faithfull's room! I'm sure he has plenty!"

"Stop it, John!" my mother cried, kicking my father's hands away from her, "*Get away from me! Stop!*"

"Get me some rusty ones! Preferably the ones Jeanette used!" he continued, but I didn't move. "Hopefully, they still have some

74

THE LIGHT WAS GOOD

blood on them..." I was confused. Did he really want me to get the scissors or was he playing a sick mind game?

"John, *please! Stop this!*" my mother didn't acknowledge me. She was focused on keeping her legs together while my father tried parting them, but it didn't seem like he meant what he was ordering. Had he wanted to part her legs, he would've. He was stronger. He was using me as a piece within his game, so I stayed put.

'Do you use me for anything, Superiorii Phorgiveness?'

'I use you for your friendship, Jane... Why do you ask?'

'It seems like I benefit from our relationship far more than you do and I wonder if there's something behind that... That somehow you're reaping benefits I haven't noticed...'

'I don't know, but you should ask me tonight, Jane.'

"*Are you going to keep speaking out of turn, Joan?!*"

"*No, John!*" her voice cracked.

She hid her scrunched up face, muffling her weeps through her palms. My mother cried a lot. Even when my father wasn't hurting her, I heard her crying into the deep hours of the night when he was asleep. She didn't need a reason to cry and her tears usually weren't sparked by anything, but she wasn't alone in her habit. There were plenty of women, little girls, little boys, and men who broke down in the privacy of their rooms, not knowing why, and they would confess their feelings to my father. They thought it was a sign the Fos Terata was persecuting them. When I escaped the underground, I realized it was the stress that plagued them, but their guilt stemmed from not having a basis of comparison. We lived in far better circumstances than those on the outside. That's what the Superiorii told us. We thought our world was normal and blessed, so feeling miserable meant there was something impure about us.

"*Are you crying, Joan!*"

"No, John!" she lied.

My father couldn't tolerate crying. There was no reason when we were the Antifasi's chosen people. He said it was a sign of ingratitude.

'What do you think about crying, Superiorii Phorgiveness?'

'I've seen you cry before, Jane...'

'That's true, but do you have an opinion on it? My father considers it something to be ashamed about... Do you think it's something shameful?'

'I don't know... ask me tonight, Jane.'

"Are you *lying*, Joan!"

"No, John!" she lied again.

"Are you lying to me, Joan! Are you lying to the Superiorii, Joan!" The back of his hand readied itself to crash against her face. It was something he did to intimidate us. It was his way of saying, 'I'm not going to hurt you, but you know I could if I wanted to.'

'Have you ever screamed at Aunt Phorgiveness or Juliet?'

'I don't know... ask me tonight, Jane.'

'Have you ever threatened to hit Aunt Phorgiveness or Juliet?'

'I don't know... ask me tonight, Jane.'

'Have you ever *hit* Aunt Phorgiveness or Juliet?'

'I don't know... ask me tonight, Jane.'

The mention of Superiorii Phorgiveness's only daughter, Juliet, reminded me of our oddity. My father's generation of Superiorii had sons and I remember hearing my grandfather's generation all had sons as well. Could the Superiorii choose the sex of their babies? If so, why did my father and Superiorii Phorgiveness have daughters? It was apparently tradition among the Superiorii to have sons and my father wasn't one to break tradition. I personally wanted a daughter, but would've been happy to birth a son since Superiorii Phorgiveness already had a daughter.

'How do you give birth to a daughter, Superiorii Phorgiveness?'

'I don't know... ask me tonight...'

"*Jane!*" my father shouted, "Were you even *listening* to me?"

"Yes," I reflexively said. It was easy to discern my lie. All my father had to do was ask me what he was saying and if I couldn't answer correctly, I'd be his new target. However, I preemptively blocked his question by asking, "Does the..." but my lips stitched themselves shut.

"Does the *what*, Jane? *Finish your sentences!*"

"Does the Den," I breathed, "Amfisvito allow children to be used as alternatives?"

And just like Jeanette, my father looked up at the ceiling, looking for an explanation to my... stupidity.

"Of course, there is..." he slammed his bewildered stare down at me, "... are you questioning your father, Jane?"

"No, father," I answered.

"Then why did you ask?"

"Because you didn't argue Superiorii Faithfull when he said there was nothing in the Den Amfisvito..."

"You know the Fos Terata lives in questions..." he continued, making his slow walk over to me.

"I know," but Superiorii Phorgiveness told me they didn't... "It just seems odd to me that the Superiorii would argue over the Den Amfisvito when they both know what it says..."

Wasn't the Den Amfisvito clear enough? Did the Antifasi write it like an academician? Riddling it with superfluous prose so purple you forgot other colors existed? Why wasn't the text plain enough for everyone to understand? The book's rules were what his congregation needed to survive into the promised future. It was cruel of him to throw us into a furnace when we hadn't first been properly guided. However, thinking the Antifasi was mistaken and cruel consumed me with guilt. What if the questions looming inside my head were the reason for this schism in the congregation? What if I was a portal for the Fos Terata's chaos? I was singlehandedly poisoning a congregation of people with my rebellious thoughts.

'Did you lie to comfort me, Superiorii Phorgiveness?'

'I don't know... ask me tonight, Jane.'

'I can't wait that long- please! Did you lie to comfort me?'

'I don't know... ask me tonight, Jane.'

"The Superiorii never argued before Superiorii Faithfull threw his opinions around as facts! My father's generation of Superiorii never argued and the generation before them never argued *either!* Superiorii Faithfull knows *exactly* what the Den Amfisvito says just like the rest of the Superiorii... myself included! *In case you forgot!*"

"I haven't, father," I tried.

"Oh no, I think you have, Jane," he hushed, "I think both you and your mother are siding with Superiorii Faithfull... and, if I may be bold enough to say, Jane," he rhetorically asked, "If there came a day... a terrible day... where Superiorii Faithfull took over the congregation... his madness our new law... I *will* throw us into the right furnace... you first... then your mother... then me... to save ourselves from the Antifasi's wrath on this congregation... That's a promise..."

It felt so wrong. How could a father tell his daughter he would burn her and her mother alive? It wasn't my fault Superiorii Faithfull contradicted my father. I've done my best to live by the Antifasi's will. But then again... Why would the Antifasi demand his people, who he supposedly loves and cares about, his chosen people, his children, to be burned alive as well? I could understand why people who commit impurities should be punished, and even thrown into the furnace for certain crimes like using the alternative and abusing their wives, though the idea was starting to bother me, too. Shouldn't those who confess get a second chance? Or at the very least a lesser sentence than being burned alive?

"And to answer your first question, Jane..." he continued, standing over me, trapping me in my corner again, "... the reason why Superiorii Faithfull and I cannot find common ground... is because he doesn't want to... and neither do I... When you're right, you're right. Why should I corrupt my truth just because someone else is convinced of their stupidity?"

"But..." I almost cut my own tongue out. What was there to dispute? He was going to keep lecturing me or screaming at me or threatening me! There was no reason why I should've said 'but', but I said it anyways. I wasn't speaking to Superiorii Phorgiveness, the cordial host of questions who blanketed his guests with warm answers. I was speaking to my father, the judge, jury, and executioner of questioners. There was no reason why I should've said 'but'... I did not want to continue talking to him.

"But... what...?" he growled, warning me to watch my tongue, though it was too late.

"But..." I paused, "...I never forgot... how well you know the Den Amfisvito... I know you're guiding us down the right path... I was just confused over why Superiorii Faithfull disagrees with the Superiorii when he should already know what to do... but now I know it's because he's dumb... I'm sorry I didn't ask very well, father... I didn't mean to upset you..."

My father's tension subsided with my flattery. He accepted my apology, but warned me to better phrase myself in the future. Trouble will follow me down long paths if I didn't watch my tongue better. Afterwards, he turned his attention towards my mother, picked her up from the floor, and gave her a dry pardon. There was no warmth in him towards her. Nonetheless, she tried hugging my father who rejected her. His responsibility as a husband was done when she had me… but when was the last time my mother was hugged?

'That was impressive, Jane.'

'Thank you, Superiorii Phorgiveness.'

'What were you going to ask, though?'

'I'll tell you tonight, Superiorii Phorgiveness.'

Chapter Six

Superiorii Phorgiveness bundled me up tightly within his arms as I climbed onto his lap. I saved so many questions throughout the day, yet we were sitting in silence. He asked me if I wanted to talk about Jeanette or my parents or the 'conversation' I witnessed between Superiorii Faithfull and my father, but I told him I wasn't ready. I didn't know where to start let alone how to adequately ask my questions. I already made a fool out of myself with Jeanette and my parents. I didn't want to embarrass myself in front of Superiorii Phorgiveness, too. He never made me feel dumb on purpose, but his intelligence naturally made me feel... stupid.

"I don't want to push you into talking if you don't want to Jane, but I can tell something is weighing on your mind."

"There is," I admitted, "but I don't know how to tell you... or if I should."

"Do you know why you feel hesitant?" he asked, but I hesitated in answering... I trapped myself within an inception of hesitation.

"Because..." I started, "... well... um..." he waited on my answer. His stare wasn't studious like before with Superiorii Faithfull and my father. It was softer. Much softer. "... I have questions to ask you... I want to know your opinion over some things..." I regretted asking his opinion because it revealed my lack of confidence. I didn't trust my opinions. How could he love someone who didn't trust themselves? "... but... I..." I stalled. I could feel the words ticking out like clockwork regardless, '... don't want to be stupid... don't want to be stupid... don't want to be stupid...'

"Then we'll have plenty to talk about," he smiled, "because I have questions to ask you, too," he confessed, saving me from finishing such an embarrassing claim.

"Did I do something wrong?" I cowered. Why would he ask me anything unless I did something wrong?

"I don't know," he laughed, "did you?"

"I don't think so..." I answered, but then I thought about my day... I had publicly questioned my father, dodged Jeanette's questions so poorly she assigned me with an opinion I highly disagree with, lied about my opinion over the congregation's rules, dishonored my father, lied to my father, and then tricked him into believing my lie by changing the conversation. Not to mention, lying to Superiorii Phorgiveness about thinking I hadn't done anything wrong, "... actually..." I corrected, "... I think I've done a lot of wrong things today... including lying to you, Superiorii Phorgiveness..."

"How dare you..." he said with a severity in his tone which stole his identity and replaced him with another from the congregation, but he thankfully couldn't keep his composure. He started laughing at himself, though, of course, I thought he was laughing at me, and hugged me even tighter, "That's okay, Jane, I forgive you, but what did you lie to me about?"

I couldn't help myself from blushing. The same way my body betrayed my will and shook without cause, I smiled like a fool and couldn't regain my neutrality. "I... I said I didn't think I did anything wrong when I did... I lied to my father and questioned him... publicly... and I embarrassed myself in front of Jeanette."

He looked at me with this thin veil of horror shrouding his face, but the veil was transparent enough to see the smile hiding beneath it. "How... utterly... shocking..." he gasped, but he laughed again, "... that's enough reason to throw you into the left furnace!"

"Really?" I whimpered, but he laughed even harder.

Despite my insecurities, I enjoyed feeling him laugh. He was a belly laugher. Every time he laughed, his belly popped me against his knees and I'd fall back onto his chest. Pop, fall, pop, fall, pop, fall until he calmed down which took some time. He cried when he laughed. Made sounds through his relief, panic, and joy. Whenever it seemed his pleasurable torment was over, he breathed out high pitch sounds, swiped away tears, remembered what happened, and laughed all over again. His laughter made me laugh, even if he was laughing at me, though it wasn't with the malice I felt, I was glad I made him laugh so heartedly. He deserved it.

That's how you know someone loves you. Do they laugh when you laugh heartedly? If they don't, if they get annoyed by your ugly laughter, those pig-like sounds, the tears, the distraction, and impatiently wait until you're done, then they don't love you. Only someone who loves you can see the beauty in your cheerfully ugly moments and grow happy at seeing you so joyful especially if they're the reason you're laughing.

"Thank you, Jane," he finally exhaled, swiping some final tears away, "I love laughing."

'And I love you...' I almost said, but the words wouldn't dare cross the threshold of my teeth. They weighed upon my tongue, holding their ground, subverting my tongue's sinister plan concocted against my best interests. I was mute for a second or two until what little reasoning I had caught up with my feelings and arrested the tongue for its treachery.

"I know..." I blushed, "... and you're welcome."

I confessed my feelings in code. My damn tongue was a cryptic, elusive traitor.

"So," he cleared his throat, "tell me... What did you lie to your father about? What did you question? And why do you think embarrassing yourself in front of Jeanette is an impurity?"

I took a cold breath in, but the wind heated in the sauna of my mouth, "I told father I was listening to him when I wasn't..." I began, "and then I changed the conversation before he could prove I was lying to him... And I questioned his understanding of the Den Amfisvito because Superiorii Faithfull said there isn't a passage that excuses... alternatives..." I took a breath and continued, "But father says there is and I don't want to question his reading of the Den Amfisvito. I'm his daughter, not Superiorii Faithfull's, and I should to take my father's side."

"I see," he nodded, "and what about Jeanette?"

"I... I..." I stuttered. I knew I didn't keep my composure, but I couldn't fathom the words to explain it. I could only explain my error inside my head, "... I... don't quite know... I tried being smart about how I answered her questions, but she got defensive and... I just... grew scared? No, no, I didn't grow scared," I corrected, "I grew nervous. I was nervous she was going to step on me... I think... I felt like she was going to step on me..."

"But you're taller than Jeanette," he smiled.

"... I know," I smiled, "but that's how I felt... I couldn't think of a smart answer... and when I took too long, I grew embarrassed and she started... attacking me... her and her followers... Her followers can't do anything without her, yet they can scream at me when they're together... When they feel stronger than me..."

"Do they usually hurt you, Jane?" he asked, but his humor was gone. I knew he cared about me, but my insecurities were thick storm clouds which blocked the sunshine of his tenderness. Little reminders like these, though, the shift from his light-hearted mood into the protection of a sheltering lion, keeping his little cub safe, tossed my heart beneath a sliver of sunlight which punched its way through the clouds. They could make up for anything bad in my life.

"No..." I said, trying not to smile, "... this was the second or third time."

His blue eyes calmed, but questions lingered on his lips.

He wanted to say something, but swallowed his words and said, "I'll keep an eye on you when you're with them from now on... If I notice you shaking, I'll pull you away." I nodded, but what was he going to say before his promise?

"But... wouldn't that mean you'd be lying?"

"Yes," he shrugged, "are you going to throw me in the furnace over it?"

"No," I laughed, "but... isn't lying... bad? Or are the Superiorii allowed to lie?"

"Oh..." he sighed, "... lying... is... necessary. Everyone lies in one way or another, so I'm not the only one committing this 'impurity', but where their lies save them from losing social ties, mine saves my life... and the lives of others..."

"What do you mean? Are you lying for someone else?" I asked, feeling a slice of jealousy.

He smiled down at me, his eyes wide, his lips tight, he was blushing. "Yes," he answered, "I'm protecting some of the most important people in my life..."

My heart sunk. He cared about other people? I wasn't special to him? "Am I one of those people?" I asked like a dog begging for scraps.

"Yes," he answered again, nodding his head with one swift bow of the chin, "in fact, you're the one I'm protecting most..."

So, he did lie to me about portals and questions. I refused to ask for confirmation on his deceit, choosing ignorance over truth, but it didn't make sense for a member of the Superiorii, especially one as kind and considerate as Superiorii Phorgiveness, to worry about his life... What was his lie? Or lies? "Is it bad to lie to a member of the Superiorii?" I asked.

"The Superiorii say lying to the Superiorii is a grave 'impurity' and those caught will be punished, but that's a bit..." he looked up towards the ceiling which made me feel stupid, though I couldn't understand why, and pursed his lips. I was so stupid I was making Superiorii Phorgiveness stupid by association... slowing down his wit... his language... "...convenient... don't you think?"

"What's 'convenient'?"

"It means something that fits perfectly within someone's plan."

"Are the Superiorii planning something?"

"Not together, but they each have their own plan."

"What about you?"

"What about me?"

"Do you have your own plans for the congregation?"

"Would you follow me if I did?" his brow curled.

"I would!" I smiled proudly, "I'd listen to everything you told me."

"What happened to taking your father's side?" he chuckled. It was his trap I readily laid my neck upon and it snapped me. Curse my blind faith.

"Oh..." my lips tightened. My heart buzzed into a defensive panic at feeling Superiorii Phorgiveness mock my loyalty, "but I don't understand why Superiorii Faithfull is so certain there's not a passage in the Den Amfisvito about alternatives when my father says there is! Is Superiorii Faithfull lying or is he reading the Den Amfisvito wrong? And how come the Superiorii can't agree when they all read the same book?"

"Superiorii Faithfull isn't lying," Superiorii Phorgiveness tried explaining, "He could be wrong... but he could also be right. It depends on who you ask... We were all taught how to read by our fathers, but-..."

"But you all have such different ideas!" I interrupted, exorcising the knots from my veins. The little solace I felt at expressing myself freely, defensively, with emotion was addicting. The sensation was akin to biting down on a sore tooth and enjoying the pain radiating through your gums, striking the jaw. "Superiorii Faithfull and father argue over children being used as alternatives while Superiorii Depherence abuses them! They argue over whether cutting off one's secret parts is what the Antifasi wants and how going after those suspected of impurities without mercy could be a good or bad thing! You even disagree with the Superiorii! Father told me the Fos Terata attack through questions, but you told me they don't! No matter what, I'll always believe you," another cryptic love confession, "because if anyone's reading the Den Amfisvito correctly, it's you, I know it's you, but it's confusing how so many people have such... violent ideas that don't agree with each other when there's only one Den Amfisvito that's supposed to protect us!" I paused for his reaction, but Superiorii Phorgiveness didn't say anything immediately. I imagined he was disgusted by my 'passion', so I continued ranting to put off hearing his judgement, "And father told me before Superiorii Faithfull started throwing his ideas around as facts, the Superiorii never argued each other! They were always in agreement! So, now I'm scared the Fos Terata do live within questions, but you told me they didn't, so I wouldn't be scared... What if I'm the reason this confusion is happening? What if I'm poisoning the congregation? Why can't I be like everyone else and not think! What if I made Superiorii Faithfull confused and my father angry and Jeanette hurt herself and-...?

"Breathe in Joan..." Superiorii Phorgiveness inhaled. His chest expanded until I was leaning against his knees again. He exhaled longer than he inhaled and then told me to breathe again, so I did.

Breathe in...

    ... breathe out.

    Breathe in...

    ... breathe out.

    Breathe in...

... breathe out.

Breathe in...

... breathe out.

Breathe in...

... breathe out...

Breathe in...

... breathe out.

We breathed together... sharing each other's air...

"Do you feel better, Jane?" he asked, brushing my snapping nerves into place. I was so busy ranting I hadn't noticed I was shivering in his arms.

I nodded because I didn't want to say anything. I was too embarrassed... 'How stupid do you have to be to shake for no reason whatsoever?'

Superiorii Phorgiveness brushed my arms, rocked me back and forth gently and in silence for a moment or two, and explained, "You're confusing reading with interpreting," he corrected, "I was taught how to read by my father and his father before him and so on and so forth until the first generation just like the other Superiorii. However, the reason why there's so many disagreements between the Superiorii now, or... just between your father and Superiorii Faithfull really, is because when they read it, they come up with different opinions over what certain passages say... That's why your father says there's a passage excusing alternatives while Superiorii Faithfull says it doesn't exist. They're interpreting the passage differently... but even in the past, the Superiorii argued over other matters, too. They never argued like they do now, but that's because they were quiet, old men who preferred to argue behind closed doors. Superiorii Faithfull isn't traditional... and both he and your father have... tempers..."

He saw it, too... It was noticeable... I thought my father's

THE LIGHT WAS GOOD

rage was the norm… camouflaged within society… but Superiorii Phorgiveness pointed his rage out like an oddity… I wasn't insolent in thinking his temper was wrong… It felt good to be right for once, "What's 'interpretation', Superiorii Phorgiveness?"

"It's what you understand from something you read and what you think it means," he answered.

"But… isn't it clear?"

"No," he laughed, "apparently, not at all."

"What does the passage say?"

"It says something along the lines of…" he took a moment to recall the passage while I readied myself for the Antifasi's demand. If I, a mere little girl, could deduce what four members of the Superiorii could not, I would return peace and bring civility into our congregation again. It would redeem the evil I welcomed in and make amends with the Antifasi. For the first time, there would be a woman member of the Superiorii, accepted for her immense wisdom and a clearly chosen favorite of the Antifasi. Superiorii Phorgiveness will fall helplessly in love with my intelligence, the Antifasi will kill his wife as a gift to me, we'll get married, Juliet will be thrilled to have me as her new mother, though she's older, but we'll be friends, and I'll give birth to her little brother. The moment was upon me. The realization of my dreams at my feet. Superiorii Phorgiveness parted his lips, narrowed his eyes, and finally said… "'Upon reaching maturity, in the days when you've had thy children, turn towards the children of the congregation for comfort.'"

    … the passage was pathetic. This was what all this trauma was over? This one little passage could mean anything! It didn't even make sense. Who turns towards a child for comfort? Children are supposed to turn towards adults not the other way around.

"Does… does that mean anything?" I asked.

"No," he answered, "that's my interpretation... It means nothing."

"Then, why did the Antifasi write it into the Den Amfisvito? And why wasn't the Den Amfisvito clear enough, so there was no room for interpretation?"

"I have answers, but I'll give them to you later," he teased. His denying drove me mad because I was sure if I was older or a boy, he would've told me, but because I was neither, he thought I wasn't ready. But I was ready! I could learn anything and take it! I was intelligent and capable if I was given the tools to accomplish my goals! The education! The chance!

"But why not now?" I whined.

"Because I want to answer your questions before I forget," he reminded, "you did say you had a lot of questions for me, right?"

I was so absent-minded, running from topic to topic without a care for the ones we ran past. He was intelligent enough to keep me on course, but I didn't want the course. I wanted to structure myself. It was impossible for someone like me to change my ways. Yet, another flaw to feel ashamed about... my lack of an attention span. Not to mention, I had just whined like a spoiled child... a child... how humiliating... in front of my love... my worst fears had spindled their way to fruition.

"Oh... right..." I swallowed, doing my best to pick up the questions I dropped, one by one, along our conversation, but I couldn't remember anything. The electric questions were the only ones sparking my mind, 'What do I mean to you?' 'How do I make you happy?' 'Have you ever abused your family?' I didn't dare ask them. How did I even consider them in the first place? When I finally snagged on a proper question, though, relief lightened time, "How do you have a daughter?" I asked.

Superiorii Phorgiveness's soft smile dropped to stone. His grip on me loosened, but he still held me like a babe within his arms. "Well..." he swallowed, "... soon enough you're going to need to know... and I pride myself in telling you the truth... but... um..."

"Is it bad?"

"No, no, no, it's not bad- well, I mean... it can be... but it depends on who your husband is... but you have to do it to have children... and it shouldn't be bad... but men-..."

"No, I don't care how children are made," though, on second thought, I did, "I just want to know how daughters are made."

"Well..." his brows furrowed, "... it's the same way, Jane," he laughed.

"No, it's not..." my head shook, "... It can't be... At least not for the Superiorii."

"What do you mean?"

"The Superiorii always had sons because it's more... *convenient*," I smiled, leaning into him, reminding him of how good a student I was, "but you and my father chose to have daughters... And I want to know how you make one because if I had to choose between giving birth to a boy or a girl, I'd want a girl... unless..." My mind was too late. It was almost close enough to grapple my tongue, throw it to the ground, and make its arrest when, in a last-ditch effort, my tongue skidded the word 'unless' through my teeth.

"Unless...?" he echoed.

"Nothing!" I hurried, "How do you have a daughter?" and then I asked questions to distract him from my slip, a new, handy habit, "Why did you choose to have a daughter, especially when the Superiorii had sons, and why did you name her Juliet?"

"I didn't choose..." he began, smiling again, but his soft smile was dotted by blue, stormy pools, miserable and dreary, hanging above his lips. His pupils were drowning.

"You didn't choose...?" I asked, almost whining again.

"... no... I'm surprised you noticed that," his cheeks tightened, "I never noticed the pattern," he laughed, "though, I'm sure there's been a few daughters here and there throughout the generations, it just so happens the past two didn't have any. It's a coincidence, Jane... nothing more."

"What's a 'coincidence'?" I asked.

"It's when something looks like it's been done on purpose, but it's just an accident," he promptly answered, "and I liked the name Juliet... When I was younger, I had imaginary friends... friends inside your head..." he elaborated, "and one of them was named Juliet... She dated my other friend Romeo," he noticed my puzzled face, utter bewilderment at the name 'Romeo', and said, "I know, a name that doesn't start with the letter 'J'- how impure!" I laughed and felt elated I had something in common with Superiorii Phorgiveness. We both had imaginary friends! "I always felt bad for her, though... my imaginary friend, Juliet... I knew she was stuck in a world she didn't want to be in, so I stopped thinking about her to free her... Then, my Juliet was born and I felt like... it was a suitable name for a girl born here."

I ignored his reasonings and rushed into flattery.

"If I was your imaginary friend, I wouldn't feel stuck inside your head," I smiled. It was my most daring way so far of telling him I loved him.

"If you were stuck inside my head, Jane..." he sighed, dramatically, "...I'd be dead," The thought of me literally being stuck inside his skull threw me into hysterics and I laughed in my ugly, loud, close to dying way.

"I'm glad you find my death so amusing, " he said dryly which made me laugh so hard I couldn't breathe anymore.

Sarcasm. I didn't know what it was, but I knew it was hilarious.

Chapter Seven

The morning after was a special occasion. We were prompted to hunt for hidden evils looming within our hearts. If we found something treacherous, something as simple as a new interest, a new infatuation, growing between our beating walls, we had to rip it from ourselves before it rotted into thoughts, questions, and spoiled into actions. The warning was redundant, but it carried heavier meaning during Superiorii Depherence's sermon. It was apparent why within moments.

Superiorii Phorgiveness and Superiorii Faithfull led a long man up the two steps of the platform while he clumsily toppled over his left after each lift of the knee. Superiorii Phorgiveness, standing on the man's left, was the man's shoulder to cry on. Both Superiorii carried him to judgement and left him behind to suffer alone. The man was untied, free to run away, yet he stood beside Superiorii Depherence in tears. He was quaking with fear, so frozen his wet chin was stuck to his chest and his eyelids had cooled together. Dirty, but unbruised, he looked like one of us minus the tears. I recognized him, but I never spoke to him. He was another face in the crowd until that day. I sat in the third row from the front to the right with my mother and could see a short, swollen vein bulging from his tall forehead. I wouldn't have been shocked if he had soiled himself, considering the unusual, mustier smell in the air.

I looked for an inclination of pity in Superiorii Phorgiveness's countenance, but he sacrificed nothing. He was scanning over the congregation, ignoring me, with the same silent stare he had whilst staring at my father and Superiorii Faithfull the day before. Analytical, calculating, observant. The corners of Superiorii Faithfull's lips were tinged with the pity I expected from Superiorii Phorgiveness, but his eyes were still. He looked

ANGELICA LABYRINTH

over the congregation as well, but unlike Superiorii Phorgiveness, Superiorii Faithfull focused in on one spot. I looked back
in the direction of his stare and noticed a statuesque woman sitting upright beside her sobbing son. He wasn't allowed to cry.
No one was. Anyone who cried for the guilty was siding with the
Fos Terata and could suffer the same fate. Children were at times
spared the gravity of punishment, but they weren't to be con-
soled. Even if they were crying over their father...

"Your eyes are deceiving you, my brothers..." Superiorii
Depherence began, fanning his stare over the congregation, lick-
ing his glance over each individual one by one, "If you see a
man... standing beside me..." he looked at my row, "then the
Fos Terata has blinded you!" The congregation gasped, mothers
clung onto their children, asking them if they saw a man to
which they nodded and further gasps broke out, "Do not worry,
my family! Do not worry!" the engorged man calmed, petting
his hand through the air, "The Antifasi protects those who do
his will even if they're walking amongst the Fos Terata! But
does that mean we can test the Antifasi's mercy towards us?" A
murmur of 'no' washed over the congregation, mothers looked
down at their children, expecting them to shake their heads,
and their children obeyed, shaking their heads, "The Antifasi
will burn the Fos Terata who dare attack His congregation, but
we..." he emphasized, taking a pause to fan over the left row,
staring at one person in the back, "... we must first burn their
portal..." I looked back and noticed the little, sobbing boy looking up at Superiorii Depherence from beneath his bushy brows,
reddened, wet eyes, rivers leading down his baby fat cheeks,
"If they keep pouring in... how can the Antifasi burn the ones
attacking His congregation? He would have to burn *all* the Fos
Terata!"

    'Why couldn't he burn all the Fos Terata?' I wondered,
but you couldn't test the Antifasi. It was heresy to think it and
evil to try, so, of course, I felt guilty and did my best to drown
my thoughts out by listening to Superiorii Depherence's croak-

ing voice. But I also pitied the crying man and his sobbing son. How couldn't you pity a man too ashamed to look at his shaking son for the last time? 'It's just a portal, it's just a portal, it's just a portal,' I repeated to myself, but it barely made a dent in my feelings for them.

"No, no, no, my brothers... We cannot allow the Antifasi to waste his power, now can we?" a roar of 'No!' washed over the congregation. Mothers looked down at their children in either pride or disappointment depending on whether their children shouted 'No!' as well or not. "Of course, we can't! Now... beside me..." he turned towards the crying man and waved his hand across his torso, barely acknowledging him, "... stands a portal... If you focus hard enough, you'll see it for what it is..." the engorged, bald man raised his chin and closed his eyes, "The Superiorii are giving you the strength of mind to do so now..."

Two voices from the congregation frantically whispered, "I can see it now! I can see it now!" and afterwards, most everyone could see it, too. I was too incompetent to see it, though. It was another sign of how weak-minded and spiritually stunted I was.

"Now that you can see it for what it is, my brothers, what do you intend to do with it?" Superiorii Depherence asked to which most of the congregation screamed.

"Burn it!"

"I don't think the Antifasi heard your decision, my brothers, what do you intend to do with it?" Superiorii Depherence asked again to which everyone in the congregation screamed louder.

"*Burn it!*" We all chanted including myself and the sobbing boy. I was watching him over the back of my seat because I wanted to see if he was going to scream, too. And he did.

The man collapsed in hysterics, dropping to his knees, falling over on his side, but the Superiorii picked him up and handed him off to my father who was waiting on the other side of the platform for him. They didn't force him over and my father didn't grapple at him. They walked together to the other side and gently passed the wobbling man to my father. He wasn't resisting the Superiorii or his fate. The damned usually never do.

My father held the crying man's arm and let the man rest his head against his shoulder as he ushered him past the rows. The entire congregation watched the men walk away, disappear into the left furnace room, and turned back around to look at Superiorii Depherence in anticipation for him to say, "Everyone may now stand up and make their way towards the left furnace room..." to which they did, hurriedly. There was an air of feigned cordiality with people giving others way and everyone smiling at one another as they crowded down the left, narrow hall, but it annoyed me. I would've much preferred they pushed and walked over one another like I knew they wanted to.

I tried finding the sobbing boy to see how close he and his mother would stand from the burning, but he was gone. I wormed my way through the crowd undetected by everyone I passed and found him ushered *into* the furnace room by his mother. He was shivering, a bucket of ice poured down his back, but he walked without resisting his mother like his father had walked without resisting the Superiorii. 'Do I shiver like him?' I wondered, feeling a point in my heart start to spiral out like a lotus flower blooming, 'Please help him, Superiorii Phorgiveness...' I begged. I wanted to hold the boy myself, soothe him, rock him back and forth like Superiorii Phorgiveness rocked me, but he was too far away. If only he was closer...

I didn't see the burning firsthand. The furnace room was filled with the Superiorii, the crying man's family, and a few members of the congregation. The entryway was blocked off by even more members standing tall, holding their little ones on their shoulders, jumping to see the execution. I could hear my father citing memorized lines of the Den Amfisvito, exorcising the crying man's presence from us, but his voice was buried beneath shifting bodies and murmurs. Once the hum of my father's voice stopped, there was silence. Absolute silence. Everyone held their breath... The crying man was led into the furnace, but there was no reaction. He did as he was told. Had there been a struggle, the congregation would've insulted, spat, and chanted for his death again, but there was no such exclamation. He willingly walked into the furnace... burned... and his screams shattered through the window of our silence. Excited women who raced to closer spots wailed out against the horrific sight and fainted while babies and younger children shrieked from the sound. Men grew sick from the smell and did their best to avoid vomiting on their wives who clung to them for comfort.

The crying man's screams welled me up with tragedy. I held a bundle of tears against my lower lids, but I was a clumsy woman holding fruits against her chest without a basket. They all slipped and dropped to the stone floor. 'It's just a portal, it's just a portal, it's just a portal,' I tried, but rushing thoughts whispered, 'He used to be a boy. He got married. He has a son. He's watching him die. This is how he's going to die. This is the end. He never imagined this. Here he is. He's not going to exist anymore. Everyone will forget him. His life will mean nothing. It means nothing.' His hysterics were claiming me. As his body was dying, his soul was possessing me. The same weight that collapsed him was now weighing upon me.

'You're the only one mourning him, Jane...' Was there a Fos Terata inside my head? 'He meant nothing to you before... yet now you feel strongly for him... You're feeling his feelings... Do you know why, Jane?'

'Stop, stop, stop, stop, don't think about anything, stop thinking, you don't need to think, just stop thinking,' I tried drowning the thoughts, but they were stronger than me. They were holding my head beneath water. I was too weak to control my mind.

'Portals are connected, Jane... They feel each other's feelings...

They feel each other's pains... You're feeling a portal's feelings... What do you think that makes you, Jane?'

'Stop! Stop! Stop! I don't want to think about this! I don't need to think about this! Stop thinking! Stop thinking! All you need to do is stop thinking!'

'All those questions you've asked, Jane... Some of them against the Antifasi... I wonder how many Fos Terata have slipped in because of you... You probably let in far more than the crying man... Maybe even half of all Fos Terata... That's why the congregation is so divided now... That's why your parents are suffering... You've poisoned them all... If a few Fos Terata could blind people... I wonder what half of them could do...? I wonder what the Antifasi's going to do to you for poisoning his congregation...'

'No! No! No! No! Stop thinking! Stop thinking! Stop thinking! Stop thinking! But you *have* asked so many questions, Jane... Stop it! Stop it! *So* many questions... Please! Stop! Please! Question... Stop it! Stop! Keep questioning... *Please!* Let them all in...'

'I think it's best you tell your father what you've done, Jane...'

'No...'

'The guilt will drive you mad...'

'Stop!'

'Even if you don't, the Superiorii will find you... They'll find you... and your father will burn you... Superiorii Phorgiveness will burn you... You'll be ripped apart by the Fos Terata... until you turn into one yourself...'

'Please, stop! Think about anything else! Anything else! Superiorii Phorgiveness! Superiorii Phorgiveness! Superiorii Phorgiveness! He lied to you, no he didn't, yes, he did, he doesn't love you, please stop! He'll never love you!'

'It's only a matter of time, Jane...'

When the screams quieted, most everyone settled back into a pretentious air and the Superiorii locked themselves in the left furnace room. I often wondered how they could tolerate the awful stench carrying into the main hall, but concluded it was a trick of the Superiorii. Those who fainted were carried into their rooms by members of the same sex. God forbid their husbands excessively touch their wives in public even to pick their unconscious bodies from the floor. The children now asking questions and/or still crying were also escorted to their rooms by their mothers. Their minds needed controlling and these emotional moments were the perfect time to destroy what needed to be destroyed. Their curiosity.

The only members left were older children and our parents. I stood beside my mother, imagining Superiorii Phorgiveness behind me, holding me, and barely listened to my mother's conversation with other women, including Aunt Faithfull.

'The Fos Terata don't live inside questions, Jane,' Superiorii Phorgiveness comforted, 'I thought you said you would believe anything I told you...'

'I do! There's just... things... that seem to... go against what you're telling me... I don't believe you're wrong, but... sometimes I think you might be a little... a little wrong.'

"Where were you, Aunt Loyaltie?" Aunt Faithfull asked, "I was towards the entryway and you were nowhere near it." Her hands clasped before her stomach. Witch hands. I don't think I caught a glimpse of her palms. She was so tightly bound together.

"I was with my daughter, Aunt Faithfull," my mother answered, "We were seated towards the front, so by the time we made our way towards the entryway, it had already been filled by those sitting in the back."

"I'm sure that wouldn't have happened had you put forth effort to see the Antifasi's will carried out," Aunt Faithfull critiqued, "I was sitting in the second row and managed to reach the doorway with Jeanette… and she's holding a baby…"

"Well…" my mother thought, lowering her gaze from Aunt Faithfull's face to the woman's squared shoulders, "… Jane and I are not the running types…"

"So, you *chose* not to see the Antifasi's will carried out," she taunted to which the other women furrowed their brows at my mother and two of them stole glances at me.

'Why do older women judge me? I'm half their age… I could be their daughter… Shouldn't they be mature by now? They're old and ugly enough to behave wisely… Why do they remind me of Jeanette and her friends?' I thought, trying to avoid their glares.

'Adults are bigger, wrinkled versions of children,' Superiorii Phorgiveness answered, 'Don't expect too much out of them otherwise you'll be disappointed.'

"No, I didn't. That's not what I meant, Aunt Faithfull," my mother defended, "Don't twist what I say."

"I'm repeating what you're saying, Aunt Loyaltie," she smiled, looking towards her friends confused by my mother's reaction. She was trying to make my mother feel ridiculous. "If you have a problem with what I'm saying, then maybe you should think twice before speaking."

They relished Aunt Faithfull's dominance over my mother's timidity. Shaming others was the most entertainment these blood suckers received in their miserably pious lives. They extended their delight and my mother's, or whoever else was their victim, humiliation by gossiping to those like-minded enough to listen, reliving the experience like a serial killer dressing their murdered victim. It disgusted me. I wanted to insult them, but they were older than me. No matter how clever my response was, no matter how well I dissected their personalities, countered their statements, they would scorn my rambunctiousness and attack my mother's parenting. Then, they would preach over how poor a mother Superiorii Loyaltie's wife is, how savagely her daughter behaves, and my mother and I would privately suffer the consequences at my father's tongue once he caught wind of the gossip. No matter what, these bloodsuckers will always win. And that's what infuriated me the most. I wanted to cut them down.

'What should I say, Superiorii Phorgiveness?' I asked, 'They shouldn't get away with their cruelty, but… whatever I say will make things worse.'

'I don't know, Jane,' he said, 'ask me tonight.'

My mother and I stood silent. I don't think she was thinking the same thoughts I was because she wasn't the type. She didn't think the way I did, but I'm sure she was trying to save herself the shame of an argument, so I followed suit.

"What did he do?" one of the women, Sister Honestie, asked Aunt Faithfull.

"Don't you mean 'it', Sister Honestie?" Aunt Faithfull corrected.

"Oh… yes… 'it'… I'm sorry…" she blushed as Sister Gratefull and the other two women pursed their lips at her.

"Much better," she nodded, "and *it* opened a portal between the world of the Fos Terata and our congregation, Sister Honestie," Aunt Faithfull said, "weren't you paying attention to Superiorii Depherence?"

The other women scoffed at her expense, but watched Aunt Faithfull more than they looked at Sister Honestie. I noticed Aunt Faithfull swipe a glance over her followers and realized they were all trying to impress one another. The women looked for Aunt Faithfull's approval and she looked for their… loyalty? My mother carried a stone face during this interaction. She didn't scoff, didn't purse, didn't care. She was not impressed, but Aunt Faithfull noticed that.

"You can leave, Aunt Loyaltie," she informed, "You're obviously not pleased with our company."

They caught my mother off guard with this sudden acknowledgement. Most people don't notice you unless you're doing something they don't like, for example, not paying them the attention they want, and my mother, being a mild woman, was the perfect target for someone as authoritarian as Aunt Faithfull. The hag was a commander leading an army of followers into popularity while my mother was the quiet civilian going about her life, fulfilling her little responsibilities, being uprooted by this commander's arrogance.

Aunt Faithfull waved goodbye to my mother, smiling at her, pride pouring over her eyes, her momentary fix buzzing through her vain veins, and like vomit, I couldn't help expressing myself. My disgust for her filled my blood, my pulse beat harder, the heartbeat in my temples rippled out, tripping the eye bone and diving into the pools of my dark eyes. I physically needed to say something otherwise my body would've sliced my lungs.

"Stop that…" I ordered. It was a clever response which clearly showed how unlike a child I was… I assure you.

"Stop what?" Aunt Faithfull laughed, joined by her little followers, including Sister Honestie who, only a few moments ago, was on the receiving end of Aunt Faithfull's bark. I didn't know how to respond, 'Stop being mean to my mother?' 'Stop being annoying?' That sounded like something a little girl would say. I could feel my mother's pleading eyes clutching down on me, begging me to remain silent, but I was overcome with words.

"Stop… saying… mean things…" I finally said, but I hated myself more and more with every word uttered. Every syllable clicked out.

The group of women laughed at me again, but, once again, Aunt Faithfull's followers looked at her for approval while giving me, the butt of their humor, occasional glances. With each glance they tossed me, though, I broke it and analyzed the inner machinations. I noticed in each something not entirely there. There was something devious in their stares. Something empty. I didn't know what to call it then, but I do now. They were superficial. The underground was stuffed with superficial people. Their only reason to live was to follow or be followed- obey or be obeyed- and the only vaccine preventing their infection was thinking for yourself. The Antifasi hated independent thinkers, though... They were proud heretics, arrogant and selfish, willing to poison the communal fountain with their tainted hands for a drink. Despite feeling it was Aunt Faithfull and her group's attitude that was problematic, I knew it was my crooked mentality that was wrong. Not theirs. I was stupid for speaking up. I was stupid for trying. Why couldn't I be normal? See things the way they did?

"I'm not saying mean things, Jane," Aunt Faithfull corrected, giving me her undivided attention. She refused to break eye contact with me, beating me down with her stare, wide-eyed, threatening, confident. I was starting to shake again. "I'm telling the truth... I'm an honest person..." she claimed as if my mother and I weren't honest people, too, "I don't ignore people's attitudes towards me and I don't allow people to be rude towards me either. Your mother," she gestured, "was giving me an attitude when me and my friends were having a little laugh. I noticed it and I confronted her over it."

"Stop it, Aunt Faithfull. She's a child," my mother tried, but she went ignored. These sharks had a better meal with me than they did with her.

I was just a child when it came to others' expectations of me... Remain quiet, remain obedient, value the opinions of adults over your own... I was just a child when it came to how others treated me... No acknowledgement, no respect, overlooked or looked down upon, my existence barely present... When I did something wrong, though, I was an adult. I was treated as an equal for long enough to make me feel lesser than human. Given a sudden rush of negative attention when before I was ignored. I was expected to know better, though I was expected to know nothing before. I was a perfect target. I was infantile, inexperienced with confrontations, nervous, so the vantage was Aunt Faithfull's and Aunt Faithfull's alone. However, that made me wonder... Would I be considered a girl or a woman if they found out about my questioning... would it even matter?

"If you taught your child to hold her tongue, she wouldn't receive this lecture from me, Aunt Loyaltie."

"It's my responsibility to lecture her," my mother argued, "You're trying to take charge of someone else's responsibility which I'm sure the Antifasi wouldn't appreciate. He's given us our roles to tend to and if you're busying yourself with my responsibilities, then yours are suffering, so both my daughter and I would appreciate you paying more attention on your tasks than on ours."

"My *responsibility*," she slammed, "as the wife of a *Superiorii*," as if we didn't already know, "is to make sure the congregation is behaving in accordance with the Antifasi's will." She glared at us with parted lips for a moment and continued, "You and your daughter are members of this congregation, so excuse me for caring enough to try and correct the both of you."

"You only care about what other people think of you," I snapped, but immediately, per my habit, I regretted opening my mouth. Despite trying to learn from past mistakes, keeping silent when provoked, it seemed in confrontations, I'd be doomed to suffer the same rounds of idiocy.

"Excuse me?" Aunt Faithfull begged, raising her brows while her eyes punched the sight of me.

"Apologize to Aunt Faithfull, Jane," my mother ordered, but before I could apologize, Aunt Faithfull thought it best to teach me a few lessons my mother forgot to inculcate.

"Caring about what other people think of you is taking care of your reputation. As the wife of the Superiorii, I care deeply about what other people think of me because I don't want them to consider me a fool who says the first thing that pops into her mind," she narrowed her eyes at me to emphasize this wasn't a character trait she picked at random, "You will become the wife of the Superiorii one day, so you're going to learn this lesson one way or another. Otherwise, who's going to respect you enough to take you or your husband seriously? From your current and past conduct with me and Jeanette," flashbacks from the humiliation I suffered with Jeanette zapped at my nerves and made me shake even harder, "I can tell you're going to have a difficult time applying this lesson into your life, but we both believe in you, Jane," this disgusted me. I didn't want their duplicitous support. I wanted them gone. "One day, you're going to realize I'm trying to help you... and when that day comes... I hope you think highly of me, too."

"Excuse me," Superiorii Phorgiveness said, placing a hand on my shoulder which relieved the tension from it immediately. Had I not restrained myself, I would've clung onto his hand and kissed it before everyone. "I'm going to borrow Aunt Loyaltie and Jane... Superiorii Loyaltie wishes to have them by his side when dinner is served."

"Oh! I'll accompany you, Superiorii Phorgiveness. I'm sure Superiorii Faithfull wishes to have me by his side, too," Aunt Faithfull smiled, taking on a lighter air in the presence of a Superiorii.

"No," he answered, smiling to mask the severe tone in his negation, "Superiorii Faithfull is still busy preparing the meat, but he'll be out soon. You can join him then, Aunt Faithfull."

"Oh... very well..." she responded.

Whatever talent Superiorii Phorgiveness possessed to quiet the arrogant was the talent I begged to have for myself. Until then, I was pleased to have someone as strong as him watching over me. The quantity of people who love your mask don't matter. It's the quality people which have seen your naked face and love you enough for it to protect you that matter.

"Aunt Loyaltie," he addressed, not looking my mother in the eye unlike his direct stare at Aunt Faithfull, "would it be alright if your daughter spent a little time with my family?" There was a tight silence between them. The oily moment passed through the pinch of their tension, "I'll send her back to you before dinner is served..." he assured.

My mother nodded and her voice trembled out an, "Of course," when she noticed Superiorii Phorgiveness didn't see the bobbing of her head. She walked on ahead, leaving us alone. I whipped my head up towards Superiorii Phorgiveness with a silly smile stretched across my face. 'I knew you were in love with me,' was all I could think.

"Don't eat the meat..." he warned.

"Why not?" I asked.

"Just don't eat it, Jane," he ordered.

"But... why not?"

"Please don't ask me why. I'm not going to eat it. I'm not allowing my wife and Juliet to eat it either. I can't tell any of you why, but please don't eat it."

He seemed frantic, so I indulged him. "Okay," I said, "I won't eat the meat."

C hapter Eight

Juliet was a statue. It pained me to speak to her. I tried making small talk about her family, her father especially, and asking what she thought of the burning, but nothing. She was a tomb. She either nodded or gave curt, one-word answers, no glances, no eye contact, not even a head shift in my direction. I would occasionally look up at Superiorii Phorgiveness, begging to talk to him instead of his daughter. For some reason, though, he fancied the idea of Juliet and I becoming friends, so he encouraged conversations between us by introducing new topics. Juliet refused them. She didn't want to talk to me. She didn't talk to anyone except her husband and mother. If it hadn't been for her general antipathy, I would've felt incredibly disliked by the Phorgiveness family. I received the same cold treatment from Juliet's mother, though it was more cordial than her daughter's temperament.

'Do they know about my feelings towards Superiorii Phorgiveness?' I wondered, but that couldn't be the case. Superiorii Phorgiveness met with me in secret. He told me never to tell my father about our nightly meetings, so I assume he kept our time together a secret from his own family as well.

"How's James?" Aunt Phorgiveness asked which excited me because I was finally being acknowledged. She was even curious about a detail in my personal life, though it might've only been a polite interest. Especially since she was staring intently at her empty plate, same as Juliet, both seemingly sharing some telepathic conversation regarding how uncomfortable my presence made them.

"From what I know, he's fine... He's studying regularly with my father, but also reading the Den Amfisvito alone to memorize certain texts... His health is in good standing..."

"Oh," she said, "that's nice..."

"Yes..." I nodded. My cheeks twisted in discomfort, cranking out a mechanical smile. What was I supposed to say? I looked at the empty plate before me, same as Juliet and her mother, pretending I was studying something important. Soon enough, though not soon enough, I would return to my seat. My comforting thought. I'd soon be free from this situation, this waste of time. I was sitting only a person away from the love of my life, capable of having a conversation worth having, but I couldn't take it. What is a girl doing talking to a grown man? Why are they talking about such personal and intellectual matters? I knew pushing Juliet out of the way to get to her father would expose our love affair to the world, and also to Superiorii Phorgiveness considering how it was a one woman love affair, but it was a risk my stomach considered worth taking. Boredom can flip logic on its head and make sense out of nonsense. However, my nerves kept me in check and that 'soon enough' finally came with Superiorii Faithfull announcing dinner.

"I think it's time you returned to your family now, Jane," Aunt Phorgiveness said, but I almost snarled at her because no one asked her to state the obvious. I held back, though. I knew age or disease would catch up to her, she would die, and I'd be free to marry her husband and claim Juliet as my daughter. My new comforting thought. I wouldn't mind having an adopted daughter older than myself as long as I had a daughter.

"Okay," I said, standing up.

I ignored Superiorii Phorgiveness as I walked past him, just to further emphasize our social distance despite sitting with him and his family, but on my way, I imagined how we would parent our future son together. I'd name him something daring like Romeo, breaking the unspoken rule of only giving names that start with a 'J', and teach him how to think for himself, but not question too much. At least not until I could prove the Fos Terata didn't live within questions. If they didn't, I'd teach him how to question everything. Superiorii Phorgiveness would teach him how to read, analyze, and be strong and intelligent just like him.

"Please don't tell your father about what happened with Aunt Faithfull," mother hushed as I sat down beside her while father was away serving the congregation their meals along with James, Superiorii Faithfull, and his son.

"Okay," I nodded, but I couldn't have cared less about what happened with Aunt Faithfull, or anyone, because I was still imagining my future with Superiorii Phorgiveness. Reality and memories take last place to daydreams.

Superiorii Faithfull and I were going to live together as husband and wife. Instead of having a standard room with one bed, we would hack the bed's frame and build a little fort out of wood with the mattress nestled inside. Superiorii Phorgiveness and I would sleep on the floor together, my head resting on his chest, him lulling me to sleep with his inflating and deflating chest, while our son, Romeo, slept inside the wooden fort on his comfortable bed. Romeo would curl himself up in a bundle of blankets, trying to cover his head, but his thick hair, which he would inherit from both his parents, would make it impossible for him to fully cover his head. It wouldn't matter, though. Unlike me, he wouldn't be afraid of his imagination. He would fall asleep dreaming about the fantastic characters his father would tell him instead of the Fos Terata.

"How's Juliet?" mother asked.

"Fine," I answered, curtly. I didn't have time for small talk. She was distracting me. I wanted to return to the better world I knew, deep down, was too peaceful to come true.

"That's good. Did you two talk about anything?"

"No," I answered, shifting away from her slightly to further show my disinterest. She understood and lowered her head towards the empty plate before her, picking up her chipped, old fork and wobbling it between her thumb and index finger a little above the plate.

Romeo could become Superiorii since Romeo would be Superiorii Phorgiveness's biological son. He could make the Den Amfisvito available for everyone and resolve conflicts over interpretations by demanding interpretations be weighed as opinions instead of facts, but that could only happen when Superiorii Phorgiveness passes on the title. The idea of Superiorii Phorgiveness dying left me cold. That's the only way anyone could become Superiorii. Their father or mentor had to die. Superiorii Phorgiveness and I proudly sitting front row to witness our son give sermons about the betterment of the mind rather than the evil of the outside world was an impossible one. It would just be me sitting alone.

I blew the idea away and scrubbed its residue from my mind, hoping it would never find its way back again. Forget Romeo, forget Juliet, forget the future, all I wanted was Superiorii Phorgiveness.

"Superiorii Faithfull and his family will be eating with us, so don't breathe a word, Joan," my father warned, slamming his weight down against his seat, making my mother and I jump, and afterward adjusting himself closer to the table where he could prop his elbows up and cover the stress lining his lips with his palms, "We don't want you embarrassing me like you did yesterday, now do we?" he asked, but didn't regard her.

She nodded. He was restraining himself. I could feel in his countenance he wasn't bothered by either my mother or I, but by the prospect of Superiorii Faithfull sitting with us. "And the same goes for you, Jane," he said, stretching his neck out to look at me over my mother. I also nodded and looked back at my once empty plate which was now stained with boiled potatoes, bread, and a slab of charred meat. 'When was I served?' I wondered, lamenting the gift most children, including and especially myself, have. They completely lose themselves in the plane of imagination only to rejoin reality and wonder why there's holes in their memory. I hated myself for being so absent-minded, but I comforted myself in a daydream about Superiorii Phorgiveness.

He was holding me in our little room, but not like he usually held me. He was lying flat on the floor with his head resting on a bundle of blankets stolen from the Superiorii's closet and I was resting my head on his chest like before. His arms held me tightly which elated my heartbeat and my arms tightened their grip around his neck to ground myself to the floor. I was trying to sleep, but he was gazing at me, watching me go to sleep. It was one of those peaceful, honest moments where you could watch your beloved one live unaffected by expectations. I didn't need to smile to seem happy. I didn't need to keep quiet or speak. I just existed. That's it. I could feel the warmth from his stare on my face and, out of happiness at having someone as tender as him care about me, opened my eyes and kissed him.

My picture of kissing wasn't something slobbery. It was a peck on the lips. One of those puckered, silly-looking ones fish might share. However, I find it curious how I knew what to imagine when I'd never seen anyone kiss before. Kissing wasn't practiced at weddings. There were no public displays of affection within the congregation. I'd never seen my parents kiss each other either. Despite that, I knew what I wanted to do with Superiorii Phorgiveness. It was natural, but I felt guilty thinking about something I didn't even know existed.

"Thank you for having us for dinner, Superiorii Loyaltie," Superiorii Faithfull said, announcing his, his wife's, his son's, and daughter-in-law's arrival to our table.

"It's a privilege, Superiorii Faithfull..." my father feigned, "... but to what do we owe the pleasure... a special occasion, perhaps?"

"Does one Superiorii need reason to enjoy the company of another Superiorii?" Superiorii Faithfull answered.

"No…" my father dryly said, gritting his teeth behind his lips, "… I suppose not."

Superiorii Faithfull sat himself across from my father, Aunt Faithfull sat herself across from my mother, Jeanette sat herself across from me, and Joseph, Superiorii Faithfull's son, sat himself across from where James would one day sit. Their presence at our table was like a dense air blowing me off my chair and onto the floor behind me. They all, minus Joseph, had this presence of authority which unnerved me, so I looked down at my plate, but found my imagination taking a warped turn. I saw the charred meat on my plate and thought of Jeanette's genitals. The meat didn't smell as bad as her. In fact, the burnt smell was a pleasant distraction from her rotting stench, but the image of my eating her hacked, gangrenous vagina soon slipped into my mind and I couldn't help, but physically cringe from the notion.

"Why do you shake so much, Jane?" Jeanette asked.

"What?" I answered, but I felt my mother's hand rest itself on my lap and noticed my father's glare from behind her head, "I apologize Jeanette," I corrected, "but you caught me thinking about something else… What did you say again?"

"I asked why you shake so much," she repeated.

I didn't understand why no one glared at her for asking such a rude and personal question. I shrugged and, after a moment's pause, answered, "I don't know…"

"Is it because you're sick or…?"

"I don't know," I answered again, cutting her short, hoping she, or someone else at the table, might notice my contempt towards the question. It was true, though. I didn't know why I shook. I thought there was something wrong with me, but I refused to give her the satisfaction of my guess. It would invalidate me.

"I've noticed you shake a lot," Jeanette continued in her shrill voice, "Yesterday you shook so hard my sisters and I were worried about you," 'Oh how nice of you and your little followers to worry about me,' I thought, "and I noticed you shook right now."

"I wasn't..." but I froze before answering and focused on the morbidity of my plate. If I told her I hadn't shivered, she would've asked me why I shook and if I told her I had cringed from a thought, she would've asked me what thought made me cringe and I wouldn't be able to come up with anything other than the truth or silence.

"You weren't... what?" she asked.

"Never mind."

"No, tell me," she urged, reaching across the table for my hand as I pulled it away from her.

"Jane..." my mother cautioned which, despite the softness in her tone, still caught the attention of my father who only assumed the worst had happened.

I wanted to sit in silence like father ordered and think about Superiorii Phorgiveness. "I'm not comfortable talking about this, so please stop asking," I demanded, hoping my honesty was blunt enough for even someone as audacious as Jeanette to understand.

"Jeanette is just worried about you, Jane," Aunt Faithfull interjected, clearly offended, "There's no reason for you to be so defensive against her."

My most paralyzing difficulty growing up was my inability to express myself. People knew how to phrase their illogical reality or cruel intentions better than I could phrase my observations or defense. Had I the skill, the audacity, I would've told them exactly what I thought about their little concern for me. It was a mask of kindness. Beneath the façade, they used the vulnerability of another as an opportunity to elevate their own public image. It made them feel glorious in a world where nothing you did meant anything. Doing something normal made them feel special. If you bought into their false sympathies, if you believed in their masks, they owned you. If you tried defending yourself against a cruel comment, or action, they would make you the unjust, angry, cruel, vindictive, insane person. How could they, people with such warm masks, be capable of cruelty? Obviously, it's you, the quiet, isolated one, who is the problem. Brace yourself if you have the strength to sever a 'friendship' after enough degradation. Having a relationship with someone like Jeanette, Aunt Faithfull, or most of the Superiorii would cripple you, but ending it was a grueling, anxiety-inducing punishment. Though you wouldn't notice until it was too late, during your relationship with them, the confidence was sucked out of you. They fed upon your confusion and invalidated your thoughts until you couldn't confide in your own perception. It was a long-lasting, if not, permanent disability. They'd have followers, their other donors, swarm to lick your bones clean and reassure you everything you've said, done, or are is wrong.

I recognized fragments of these ideas at that time, but didn't know how to express them. I even swept the ideas I did know as nothing more than my imagination running wild with my pain again. She wasn't as bad as I was making her out to be. I was the problem. There was something wrong with me. There was always something wrong with me.

"Jane..." my mother warned again, but my father decided he was the parent to whip their child into the civil character he wanted for dinner. My mother was, once again, useless.

He stretched his neck out again, flared his nostrils at me, and through gritted teeth, I could tell he wanted me to apologize. He didn't say anything, but I could tell that's what he wanted.

"I'm sorry," I said, "This isn't a topic I'm comfortable talking about."

"Last time I checked, Jane," my father began, as calmly as he could manage for the sake of saving face in front of Superiorii Faithfull, "No one asked what you are and are not comfortable talking about."

"If Jane isn't comfortable talking about this, then the matter should be forgotten. We will move on to another topic of conversation," Superiorii Faithfull said, addressing everyone at the dinner table with a smile. He looked at me for a little longer than everyone else and I felt grateful towards him. He was a caring man. His hot chocolate stare was a nice drink in the frigidity of our company.

After the last table was served, Superiorii Depherence stood up and thanked the Antifasi for our meal. He reminded us of how undeserving we were, yet the Antifasi still provides. He talked about the delicious gift the Antifasi gave the Superiorii for cleansing the congregation of the Fos Terata's poison. He then repeated how unworthy we were, everything the Antifasi had done for us, and how we, as a congregation, deserved only death and sat down. The congregation applauded and everyone began eating their charred meat. Our rare delicacy.

I was too distracted by Superiorii Depherence's speech to begin my meal. Why would the Antifasi consider us unworthy if he was the one who created us? Wouldn't that make his ability to create life subpar? How is the idea that we don't deserve food, or to live, when we need food divine? Why does the Antifasi want us to berate ourselves so much? Anyone who thinks they're unworthy of life because their parent expects them to humiliate themselves for their approval is a victim of abuse... but the Antifasi is pure goodness... He's loving, kind, and has provided... Yet another series of questions to feel guilty about...

"The meat is so delicious, Superiorii Faithfull!" Jeanette announced to which Aunt Faithfull nodded her head in agreement.

"Thank you, but you should also thank Superiorii Loyaltie, Superiorii Phorgiveness, and Superiorii Depherence for their help as well. We all made this meal with the congregation's happiness in mind. Isn't that right, Superiorii Loyaltie?" Superiorii Faithfull encouraged.

"Very true," my father answered, smiling. He then stabbed his charred meat with a fork, brought it up to his teeth, and ripped off a bite. Superiorii Faithfull, Aunt Faithfull, Jeanette, and Joseph all stabbed their meat with their forks and chomped off huge bites. Everyone had difficulty chewing, but they relished the burnt flavors nonetheless. My mother and I were the only ones at our table starting with the bread and potatoes. I didn't know why my mother didn't eat the charred meat first. Wasn't it supposed to be delicious?

"Oh, Aunt Loyaltie..." Aunt Faithfull frowned, pointing at my mother's plate with her soiled fork, "... you haven't so much as even touched your meat!"

"You haven't taken a bite either, Jane!" Jeanette echoed in her little frantic, shrill voice which seemed to worsen with each word.

"Oh, well," my mother lingered, "I ate it last time the congregation was gifted with it and it made me quite sick, unfortunately... I spent a day sweating, vomiting, and... well... Let's just say it's best for everyone if I don't eat it." That was a lie. She didn't eat the meat last time. She even snuck my slab off my plate and hid it within her dress, so I wouldn't eat it either. Why wouldn't she eat the meat?

"But everyone gets sick after eating the charred meat, Aunt Loyaltie!" Aunt Faithfull insisted, "It's an experience the congregation shares together to show the Antifasi we're all one."

"You might see it that way Aunt Faithfull," my mother swallowed, "but I don't wish to go through that pain again."

"But not eating the charred meat shows you're ungrateful to the Antifasi and the Superiorii!" Aunt Faithfull shrieked.

"Eat it..." my father ordered beneath his breath, though it was still loud enough for me to hear him around my mother, "… eat it, Joan."

"It's a sign of your appreciation, Aunt Loyaltie," Superiorii Faithfull warned, "If you don't eat it, I'm afraid I'll have to think lesser of you."

"And the same goes for you too, Jane," Jeanette added.

I glared at her. I hated her filthy, putrid guts and wanted whatever monster she had baking between her thighs to erase her from my life. There was an onslaught of defenses and arguments flying through my mind, physical attacks, killing her, ripping her apart, humiliating her, 'No one asked for your comment. No one asked for your perspective. Neither my mother nor I want to eat the meat for reasons which we didn't force on you, so why do you think your reasons are important enough to force them on us?' but all I could manage was that one glare. Hopefully, she understood everything with just that.

The worst part was they all knew the truth about our food… The only one who didn't know was me… but they all knew… including my mother.

"I'm finishing my bread and potatoes and would *appreciate* eating my dinner undisturbed," I said, looking Jeanette straight in the eyes.

"So, you're going to eat the meat, then?" she asked.

"No," I answered.

I was a wobbling newborn deer trying to stand its ground. My face grew flushed, my heart trembled beneath my audacity, and I wasn't breathing. I would've gasped had I drew in a breath.

"Jane…" my mother pled, but my father had grown impatient with me.

"Put the meat in your mouth now," he ordered through his teeth, "both of you."

He shifted his stare at my mother who cowered away from his glare. She looked down at her dinner, took the fork soiled with potato residue, and stabbed the meat, but hesitated in lifting it. She was thinking of an alternative. She didn't want to eat it, but everyone was staring at her. They were forcing her. Her lips tightened and curled a few times. Her fingers gathered their strength to lift the charred meat off its plate, but they floated back down when her wrist needed to turn towards her mouth. She did this twice before my father hissed, *"Joan…"*

And in a moment, I saw whatever tension my mother had, the darting eyes, the buzzing mind, the curling lips, the hesitation, vanish and replaced with nothingness. My mother was a shell again. She lifted the charred meat off the plate and placed a chunk between her teeth, hacking off a bit of its flesh. She chewed it with difficulty, the pain returning from time to time, but like the meat, she managed to swallow her feelings and finish her meal properly.

Now it was my turn.

"Jane…" said my father. Everyone, except my mother, was looking at me now, waiting.

I drew a breath and tried collecting as much composure as I could, hoping it would give me the strength to brace myself for the onslaught. I had to be loyal to Superiorii Phorgiveness. He begged me not to eat the meat and I wasn't going to eat it. "I'm not…" I breathed, "I'm not going to eat it," I said, feeling a tremor beat through my stomach. It sounded off the anxiety running through my blood and I could feel knots of regret nestling themselves into my collarbone. All I could hear was the blood pumping in my ears.

"*Eat it…*" I faintly heard my father hiss, but panic was consuming me.

"What you're doing is disrespectful to the Antifasi and the Superiorii, Jane," Aunt Faithfull scowled.

"You're shaming your father, Jane," Superiorii Faithfull said which riveted my heart with dread. I was publicly embarrassing my father, in front of Superiorii Faithfull and his family no less, which meant he might actually hit me this time.

"No," I tried, stuttering, and then the shakes began.

"That's what I was talking about, Jane! Why do you always shake?" Jeanette ordered.

"This will all be over if you just eat the meat, Jane," Aunt Faithfull insisted.

"If she doesn't want to eat it-..." my mother tried.

"*Joan!*" my father growled, "*Eat the meat, Jane!*"

"But-..." I loathe that word.

"But what? There is no 'but', Jane," Superiorii Faithfull steamed, "This is your father telling you to do something. If your father tells you to do something, then you do it. Is that understood?"

     I couldn't breathe. I was inhaling deeply, plunging my chest in and out with all my might, but there was no air. I was shaking too hard for proper inhalation. My heart was beating against my chest with a fury that added to my terror because I feared it would break a rib. 'Why do I have to listen to him just because he's my father? Why do I have to listen to anyone? Why can't I just listen to myself? Why I can't I just listen to Superiorii Phorgiveness?' More and more questions to add onto my long list of guilt.

"Is that understood, Jane?" Superiorii Faithfull growled in his rough, baritone voice which almost made me cry from the jump. I nodded reflexively and picked up my fork, but I still hesitated. Superiorii Phorgiveness told me not to eat the meat.

"Eat it, Jane!" Jeanette demanded.

     He didn't even tell me. He begged me not to eat the meat.

"Is this really how the daughter of a Superiorii behaves?"

"You're really disappointing me, Jane. I thought you were better behaved than this."

"*Jane...!*" my father cried.

I stabbed the charred meat and lifted it off my plate, but waited. I was shaking. My heart was beating hard enough for the room to hear it over their conversations. 'Superiorii Phorgiveness will sense I'm in trouble and come to my rescue,' I thought. 'He promised to rescue me whenever he sees me shake... but he can't see me... I won't be rescued this time... Can't he read my mind? Or at the very least read my heart?'

"What are you waiting for, Jane?" Aunt Faithfull whined.

"I think you've been the center of attention for quite enough time now, Jane. Eat the meat," Superiorii Faithfull ordered.

"Are you really this desperate for attention?" Jeanette swiped. It was the cliché attack. It said both 'you are unloved' and 'stop trying to make us love you, you are unlovable.' She had to hide her hinting smile to keep her nature a secret, but I knew her secret. I wasn't strong enough to break the lock on her mask, but I knew she was pleased with my suffering.

My father, a human conduit of rage downloading his wrath into his core and saving it for later, remained quiet.

'Superiorii Phorgiveness,' I chanted within my head, 'Superiorii Phorgiveness, Superiorii Phorgiveness, Superiorii Phorgiveness,' but it wasn't working. I couldn't summon him

I brought the meat closer to my lips and continued chanting for my savior. 'Superiorii Phorgiveness, Superiorii Phorgiveness, Superiorii Phorgiveness,' but soon enough, like my mother, the meat passed my lips and I removed the fork from my mouth without the food stabbed on it. I was eating the meat... I chewed and chewed and chewed, having difficulty breaking it down into smaller pieces, little snags of tendons too hard to snap, and eventually just swallowed it in bigger chunks. The flesh filled my throat and rolled down my esophagus, choking me a little, but I did my best not to react. I didn't need any more attention.

"There," Superiorii Faithfull announced, waving his hand in my direction, proud of himself for having made both my mother and I obey him, but in disbelief that something so trivial could be so problematic.

I betrayed Superiorii Phorgiveness. He begged me not to eat the meat... but I did it anyways. How could he ever love someone as weak as me? How could he ever consider me his friend again? I couldn't even keep one promise...

"Superiorii Loyaltie," Superiorii Faithfull said, adjusting himself towards my father, "I wanted to discuss your sermons again because it seems we still don't see eye to eye, but I think a more pressing matter has just risen to my attention," he folded his hands before him and leaned into my father's space, trying to embitter the blow he was about to cast, "How can anyone respect the Superiorii if the Superiorii can't control their own family?"

And with that my coffin was sealed.

C hapter Nine

When I saw Superiorii Phorgiveness resting in our little room, smiling at me, waiting for me, I broke down. My chest flashed in and out, clicking off my tears, and I sobbed my way across the expanse. I managed to close the door behind me, but barely made it halfway through the room before Superiorii Phorgiveness rushed towards me. He wrapped me up in his arms, a hand supporting the back of my shaven head, hushing and rocking me as I slobbered over his shoulder, but I couldn't hold him back. He was going to yank himself away when he found out I ate the meat.

He scooped me up and carried me to a deeper part of the room. I treasured the seconds I rested my head against his chest, believing they'd be my last. He then lowered himself onto the stone floor against a corner where he could tightly bundle me up.   I tried calming myself, but the pressure was too much. My chest heaved and let out a choked shriek of frustration. He was going to hate me. He was going to push me off him. He was going to regard me as another liar within the congregation. I betrayed him. The man I loved. The only person who liked me. I shook hard, but I froze within silent screams. I wanted to keep crying because it kept me from having to tell him what I had done. It kept me from having to tell him everything my father had done.

"Just let it all out, Jane..." he soothed, brushing his fingers over my scalp while pressing his cheek against my skull, still rocking me back and forth, "... I'll wait until you're ready to talk."

I didn't want to talk. I never wanted to talk again. It was my big, stupid mouth that kept getting me into trouble. If I hadn't said anything to Aunt Faithfull, then I wouldn't have started shaking and Superiorii Phorgiveness wouldn't have approached me. If I hadn't promised not to eat the meat, then there would've been no promise to break in the first place and I would've been free to eat my meal in peace. If I had done what I was told instead of insisting on my defiance, then my father wouldn't have been humiliated. If my father hadn't been humiliated, then he wouldn't have screamed at me. He wouldn't have threatened to throw me in the left furnace for publicly shaming and defying a member of the Superiorii. He wouldn't have tried slapping me only to stop himself right before he made contact just because he knew it would leave a mark. His daughter couldn't walk around the congregation with a bruised face without there being some speculation among the bloodsuckers. He wouldn't have called me a waste of a perfectly good son. He wouldn't have kicked me out and told me to find another family to sleep with for the night.

"Do you want me to tell you a story, Jane?"

I felt guilty for nodding my head, but I wanted to take advantage of my last night with him. I was using him... No one would blame him for hating me when he found out the audacity I had for asking more of him while I still had the chance.

He smiled. I could feel his lips tighten against my forehead and I was delighted to be his reason for smiling. From this night forward, my presence would be his reason for discomfort. "There was once a man named... Dorian," he began, smiling grandly to himself now, "Dorian Oscar Gray Wilde..." I thought Superiorii Phorgiveness was highly creative for making up such unusual names. I'd soon find out he never made them up on his own. "This man was a very beautiful man who walked around without a care for the world. He would always be very kind to those who hated him and compliment them whenever he could. He did this not because he wanted to keep the peace, but because he knew it would annoy them. He loved annoying people. It was his passion other than being beautiful. Whenever someone told him something was good or bad, he would tell

123

them they were wrong. Things aren't just good or bad. They're boring or interesting," I giggled a little at this, "No one gave him their opinion because he would tell them the only thing you could do with 'advice' was pass it on because it wasn't useful to anyone. When a miserable member of the congregation known for making other people's lives impossible died, he said some people cause happiness wherever they went and others whenever they went," I laughed harder at this, but the harder I laughed, the harder I would soon sob, "There was once a foolish enough sister who thought she was smart enough to tell Dorian Oscar Gray Wilde how he should and shouldn't behave. She lectured him on his reputation and told him to be careful with what reason he gave other brothers and sisters to talk about him. Do you know what he said to this foolish sister?"

I took a couple deep, chopped up breaths and shook my head. I was too emotionally confused to think.

"'There is only one thing worse in life than being talked about and that is not being talked about,' and then he walked away," Superiorii Phorgiveness giggled, "Could you imagine telling Aunt Faithfull something like that? Or Jeanette? Could you imagine how they would react to you walking away from them, not caring what they had to say or what they thought of you?" The idea would've been tantalizing had that day not happened, but I was reminded of my shame. I curled myself up even tighter and tried pushing the memories away. I didn't want to think of anything other than Superiorii Phorgiveness... though I knew I'd probably spend the rest of my life thinking about him... "Eventually, he found a Fos Terata within the congregation that promised him youth and beauty forever if he became a portal. Do you know what Dorian Oscar Gray Wilde said?"

I shook my head.

"Dorian Oscar Gray Wilde said yes," he smiled, "The only reason he didn't say yes faster was because he thought it would make him look ugly to say anything too quickly, but he was in total agreement. He even thanked the Fos Terata for the opportunity," he laughed.

I smiled at such absurdity, but couldn't quite wrap my mind around Dorian. Was I supposed to like this character? My brows knitted in unpracticed thought.

"Why the confusion, Jane?" Superiorii Phorgiveness asked, smiling down at me.

I swallowed as many knots in my throat as I could, but felt my throat still quiver as I readied myself to say, "So... Dorian's the villain?"

"He's not the hero or the villain," Superiorii Phorgiveness answered.

But aren't all people either good or bad?

"And then what happened...?" I asked, feeling my bottom lip wiggle from tears soon expected. There might've not been any good or bad people in this story, but in real life- I was a bad person... and I knew that. It killed me inside.

"Madness..." his eyes widened with a faint smile warming his face.

If the Fos Terata could make deals like this, I hoped they'd make one with Superiorii Phorgiveness and preserve his beauty forever. He was too good-hearted to be used as a portal. "People turned into paranoid freaks and accused others of evil without reason. Some even threw those they thought were portals into the left furnace, ignoring the Superiorii's place in the matter. But the Superiorii were also insane! They claimed they could read the congregation's minds and warned anyone caught thinking evil thoughts to turn themselves in otherwise they'd humiliate them before their execution. A lot of people did, but they weren't evil. They just thought things that made them feel guilty because thinking itself felt wrong. Nonetheless, they were burned, too.

"People grew sick from the smoke. The awful smell of human

corpses burning filled the congregation and to make matters worse, there was a food shortage. Even more people died from hunger and more living people grew sick because of the dead. It was an endless cycle! Not to mention, the only people still alive and healthy were those you didn't want alive and healthy. The ones who gossiped and criticized everyone else, including the sick... They accused one person after another for causing their misery. The remaining members of the congregation along with the Superiorii, still leading them, decided there was someone within the congregation bringing this pestilence upon them. They couldn't keep executing people at the rate they had been because almost everyone had died, so they came up with a better plan... Do you know what they thought was a good idea?"

I shook my head and continued looking at him in expectation. Whatever it was, it had to be stupid because Superiorii Phorgiveness was smiling a certain way that gave away his thoughts on something he found absolutely ridiculous.

"They decided to torture people into confessing," Superiorii Phorgiveness laughed, "and guess how many people confessed to being guilty..."

"Two?" I answered which made Superiorii Phorgiveness laugh even more. I hoped he would remember how I made him laugh.

"All of them..." he answered, "... and the Superiorii threw the rest of the congregation into the left furnace including the ones who gossiped and criticized everyone else, but guess who didn't get thrown into the furnace..."

"Dorian?"

"Yes! Dorian Oscar Gray Wilde did not get thrown into the furnace because he was the last person to be tortured and when he finally confessed to being the portal who had brought so much misery upon the now dead congregation, he was thrown into the left furnace just like everyone else was before him... but! Do you know what Dorian Oscar Gray Wilde said to the Superiorii before being burned?"

"What?"

Superiorii Phorgiveness had to close his eyes, lower his chin, and swallow his laughter to keep his composure. After drawing a breath, he opened his eyes and continued, "He noticed how ugly and charred the walls were from all the burnings and, in disgust, he turned to the Superiorii leading him to the furnace and said, 'Either these bricks go or I do...'"

We both let out a burst of laughter which we contained with our hands and continued giggling hysterically at the idea of someone being so fabulous. His stomach popped in and out, like it had before, which made me laugh even harder because I was being slammed back and forth between his knees and chest again. My grip over my mouth loosened because my muscles were too busy concentrating on whatever attack my lungs were having, so I grabbed onto his knees for support. I looked over at him through my tears and saw him crying tears of joy as well, but thankfully his eyes were closed. Otherwise, he would've caught me staring at him.

"Superiorii Phorgiveness," I called, "Superiorii Phorgiveness?" I tried again, but I was answered with the same silence. I pressed my lips together hard, hoping to suppress the nervous smile crawling across my face, and stared at the wall my knees were pressed up against. I needed to focus on something painful. Something which would grind my hopeful feelings into a pulp and numb me towards reality. I was going to be hurt by the end of the night. I needed to disappoint myself gradually for the blow to come. I didn't want to be caught unprepared and whipped off my feet.

"Jane...?" Superiorii Phorgiveness answered, calling me through his hard inhales and exhales as he calmed down from his attack of laughter, "Jane...?" he called again, probably thinking I hadn't heard him the first time. Little did he know that whenever he said my name, my heart tried running from my chest and into his arms in vain. It felt too beautifully real to be acknowledged-especially by someone you've placed on a pedestal.

"Yes, Superiorii Phorgiveness?" I answered to which he repeated himself.

"Jane...?"

"Superiorii Phorgiveness?"

"What..." he choked, "What did you... What did you want to tell me?"

I didn't want to tell him anything. I just wanted to call out his name and see how he'd react. It was more a re-flex of the heart than an initiation for conversation, but, ob-viously, I needed to say something. I just had nothing to say. I could've gone with the typical 'Never mind' or 'Nothing', but he would've insisted or tried to initiate a conversation which would've circled right back to him finding out whatever it was I was going to say. Which was nothing.

"Why did you tell me that story?" I blurted, wanting to swallow the words back up immediately because I felt it came out more childishly rude than inquisitive. I wished I could've been more delicate towards Superiorii Phorgiveness, but I was too defen-sive. His attention flustered my mind.

"Because you find death funny," he admitted which was true. The suddenness of death, its inevitably, the shock, it made me laugh. But then I remembered the crying man and felt dread consume me. Even though someone had burned alive that day, I didn't feel guilty about laughing at people dying in a story in a similar way. The only thing I felt guilty about was the possi-bility of my being a portal. I was so self-involved, self-absorbed, and selfish. It was a minor revelation of how disgusting a human being I was. "Seeing you cry breaks my heart, Jane..." Superiorii Phorgiveness continued, "...and I didn't want you to see me cry... so I made us laugh instead."

He looked at me with such care. His eyes were so soft I could've fallen asleep looking at them and this gaze was, from what I could tell, reserved only for me. He was reserved when it came to everyone else, but not with me. And I betrayed him. He had gifted me the most beautiful string of words I would treasure, think, and dream about for the rest of my life and I couldn't appreciate them. They were a knife to my heart rather than a warm caress against my broken face.

"No…" I whimpered, feeling my heart shake my eyes back into tears. I folded over and tried burying my face between my knees, but I hit my head against the brick wall on the way down. Rage injected itself into my heart and I slammed my head against the brick wall in self-hatred- once more, with teeth bared, twice more, moaning out in pain and frustration, almost thrice had it not been for Superiorii Phorgiveness. He grabbed my cut forehead and I slammed it and his hand against the wall, hurting him. His hand hurried away, but he forced it back and grabbed me with his other arm and hauled me away from the wall and into his arms like a babe. He tried rocking me back and forth, but I couldn't tolerate it. His kindness was killing me. I wanted him to hate me, to hurt me, to threaten me. I wanted him to reject me.

"Jane? What's wrong Jane? Please tell me," he begged, but his concern broke another dam which flooded me with tears and forgotten emotions. "No…" I whimpered again, shivering hard.

He pressed me against him tighter and started brushing my nerves back into place, but I resisted him. I wanted to suffer. I didn't want his undeserved help. "Jane…?" he called, but I kept trying to push him away, "Jane what's wrong? Have I done something wrong?" I shook my head, "Then, why are you pushing me away?"

"Because *I* did something wrong!" I finally confessed, but I couldn't go through with the rest. I couldn't admit it. It's one thing to know how terrible a person you are on the inside, but to allow the world to know was an entirely different matter. It became too true for tolerance.

Any other person would've taken on a sterner tone. They would've loosened their grip, furrowed their brow, beaded at me, and demanded to know what it was I did, disregarding how I felt and ignoring my tears. They would've wanted to know what sort of person I was before taking care of me because the love of most is very much conditional. Superiorii Phorgiveness's wasn't, though... "No, you didn't Jane," he assured, clicking his tongue to keep his own emotions in check while pressing my head up against his shoulder, "at most, you made a mistake... but tell me what's making you feel like this... I need to know..."

I shook my head against his shoulder, turned my head, and smooshed my cheek against his collarbone. I was facing his neck again. The sight of it was blurred through my tears and the darkness didn't help either, but its warmth was tangible. Every part of him, every nuance of his person and personality, was there to take care of me. I wanted to be taken care of by him just as long as that made him happy. I wanted to inch my way closer to his neck and give him a peck. It was an urge that my heart clamored for, but my stomach suppressed it out of fear. I knew he would've winced away had I done it.

"I..." I started, trying to distract myself from my more hopeless instincts, "... I... I hurt you..." I admitted, but it was so vague. Why was I prolonging this drama? Why was I even creating this drama? I wanted attention. I was a selfish person who thought the congregation revolved around her. I didn't deserve the floor I walked upon let alone the attention from people who had better things to do.

"The only way you're hurting me is by not letting me help you, Jane," he said, but I pouted my lips and pressed my closed eyes against his collarbone. I would've slammed my forehead against his shoulder if it was a brick wall. He turned his head, kissed my temple, and I felt a tear drop and skid across my cheek. He was crying. "I'm not going to reject you, Jane..." he assured, "... I promise I won't get angry... I just need you to tell me what's hurting you."

I took a chopped-up breath, buried my tears beneath their ducts, and opened my mouth, but soon let out a series of choked sobs and pressed my mouth against his shirt to keep the cries from being heard. 'You don't deserve this. You don't deserve this. You don't deserve this. You don't deserve him.' The thought circled through my mind like a snail sliming its way around my brain. I gathered the audacity necessary to grab him, despite my crime against him, to keep him from leaving me when I confessed. I rumpled up his shirt within one hand and clamped an arm around his neck, pressing my bleeding forehead against it, and basked beneath its warmth. "I…" I tried again, but I took a deep, cool breath and stilled myself to try and get the confession out at one go, "… I ate the meat…"

I was silent. I needed to feel his reaction. My eyes were closed, but every other sense was heightened to a biased perfection. I was waiting to feel even a flicker in his muscles, but he was still. Still and silent. "Superiorii Phorgiveness…?" I called out in my desperation.

"Jane…" he said, but there was something off in his tone. He was shocked.

"Are you mad at me?" I whimpered, looking up at him… His reaction was not one I was expecting, but it seemed eerily close to rejection in my mind. He was looking out across the room with a pitiable look in his reddened eyes. He was thinking to himself… but what was he thinking of other than leaving me?

"No," he answered, "No, not at all, Jane… Did your father force you to eat the meat?" I nodded and continued looking up, hoping he'd understand, "Then I understand…" he assured, blessing me with the comfort I needed, "It wasn't your fault… You didn't hurt me…" he continued, but then he returned to his own thoughts. "Did your mother try keeping you from eating the meat?" he asked to which I nodded.

"She said if I didn't want to eat it…" I heaved, trying to regulate my breathing pattern, "… then I shouldn't be forced to, but the others made us... She didn't want to eat it either..." I breathed, "She said it made her sick, but they told us it would be an insult to the Antifasi and the Superiorii if we didn't eat it..." my lip started wobbling again which made me bow my head back against his shoulder, "... I never wanted to be a traitor, Superiorii Phorgiveness..." I confessed, "... I never wanted to betray you..."

"Who said you were a traitor, Jane?" he asked, but before he could comfort me, I answered him.

"Father..." I started breathing hard again and I could feel the tears running up my chest, "... H-he called me a traitor... He said the only thing I am is a traitor... and I betrayed you... so he's right... He's right, Superiorii Phorgiveness... a-and then he started screaming at me... and he told me he wanted to hurt me... and the only reason he didn't do it was because my bruises would be a sign that I was a bad child... and he doesn't want the congregation knowing he's cursed with a bad child... He said I'm the reason he's so angry all the time... He doesn't want me anymore... He told me he never wanted me... He wanted a son..."

"And what did your mother do about this?" he asked, swallowing the anger in his tone.

"She tried... talking to him..." I answered, "... but he... ignored her... so... she didn't do anything." I curled myself into a tight little ball of arms and legs and pressed my bald head against Superiorii Faithfull's chest. I hadn't realized that my potato sack dress was lifted up above my hips, so my privates were pressing against his legs. Superiorii Phorgiveness didn't notice either. Instead, he brought his knees closer to him, pressed me tighter against his chest, and wrapped his arms around me, building me this little hammock made of himself. The back of my head was supported by his arm, my knees were curled up by his other arm, and I was warm. His spine was resting against the stone wall, his bottom against the stone floor, the draft probably chilled him, and he was stuck keeping this position just for me.

"I would've loved to have a daughter as smart and funny and kind as you, Jane..." he soothed, "You're not a traitor... You didn't betray him or me... and you are wanted... Never let anyone make you feel differently... Promise me you'll never think you're unwanted again, Jane..." he urged to which I nodded my head, but I was tired. "Good..." he said, "Do you want me to tell you another story, Jane...?" I nodded my head again. I needed to go to sleep...

"Once upon a time, there was a prince named Jorge... He had three brothers who were all meant to inherit different thrones to govern different lands within their father's kingdom..."

"I'm too old for fairy tales, Superiorii Phorgiveness," I moaned through my exhaustion.

"This isn't a fairy tale... Fairy tales have happy endings... and you like sad ones... right?" I nodded and resolved to keep my mouth shut. Listening to his voice was enough for me to go to sleep anyways. "Prince Jorge," he continued, "wasn't happy being a prince... He was taught how to read by his father, like his brothers were, but he wanted to know more about his kingdom. He wanted to know more about everything around him... His family, on the other hand, thought him silly for not being happy with what he had and this hurt his feelings because he wanted more than anything to be smart. So, he kept his curiosity a secret and kept searching for anything that could teach him something about the world... usually at night... He read his father's notes and his brothers' journals and the kingdom's lawbook, but none of those writings taught him anything he was happy with knowing. One night, while he was reading the kingdom's lawbook for the *seventeenth time* at his father's desk," I giggled, but continued dozing off until his words were nothing more than elevator music for my descent into dreamland, "Jorge's foot kicked the wall beneath the desk and noticed it felt hollow... Others probably kicked the hollow part of the wall before him, but unlike Prince Jorge, they didn't have the curiosity needed to look down and press their hand against it. They didn't have the curiosity needed to push aside the board blocking the hole in the wall to reveal an opening small enough for a child to fit through. They didn't have the curiosity needed to crawl inside the secret room... but Prince Jorge did and when Prince Jorge crawled inside the secret room, he found exactly what he was looking for... He found a library of books from another world..."

'What's a library?' was my last conscious thought before I reached my dreams and escaped that horrible, yet made beautiful by Superiorii Phorgiveness, day.

C hapter Ten

I drifted from my dreams, ascending back to reality. I opened my eyes, watched Superiorii Phorgiveness sleep for a minute or two, relishing the quiet, little moment, and skirted his fallen arm off my feet. I needed to get up, wake him, and return before my parents noticed me gone. Though I was kicked out, my father still expected me sleeping at our door. It was my pathetic nature to beg my father's forgiveness every morning. Any change to convention would've resulted in more shouting and punishment.

I stood up, but soon felt cold. Very cold. It wasn't the chilled sensation one gets from pulling the blankets off and exposing yourself to the day's bitter breeze. I was wet. I was wet and the draft was making the cold patch icy.

Had I pissed myself? Worse. Had I pissed on Superiorii Phorgiveness?

My hand rushed towards the spot and felt it to confirm, or hopefully deny, my suspicion. It was wet, but it wasn't piss. It was thicker than water. The fluid was denser than urine and lingered on my fingertips rather than dripping down them. I tried twirling my dress around to better study the stain, but I couldn't easily reach it. I needed to take the dress off and further inspect it, but I couldn't with Superiorii Phorgiveness in the room. We weren't married... unfortunately... I also needed to check Superiorii Phorgiveness. If I had stained him; I would've thrown myself in the furnace out of shame. If I hadn't, then I would've left before he woke up, so he didn't see my stain.

I had stained him.

It wasn't a very large stain. It was a black spot dotting his pelvis and smears around and across his waist from adjusting myself throughout the night. In my mind, though, his entire dress had been soaked with fluid; I had bathed him in it, but then it hit me... There was something coming out of me... It was dark... and heavy... like a Fos Terata... like guilt... I was bleeding out the creature inside me... There was evil inside me and it was oozing out... The shock numbed me from noticing the beast crunching at my organs, but its teeth were becoming more and more apparent. The pain was lower than my stomach and circled around my waist, pressuring my lower back and stomach into thinking I needed to use the bathroom, but I didn't. It was meaningless pain... There was something inside me... something alive... I moaned and curled over, hoping it would trap the beast, but it scattered throughout me. There was more than one inside me. A shock ran through my arms and I tightened them around me. I tried pressing my fingertips into my lower back to massage the pain away, but it didn't work. My lower stomach pinched and tightened at two points closer to my hips, shocking me back into an erect posture which hurt me far more than being slumped over. I eased myself back over my curled arms, holding myself tightly, frustrated over all my vain attempts to control the torturers within me, and glimpsed over at Superiorii Phorgiveness. He was still peacefully sleeping. Peacefully oblivious.

The portal was opening inside me... and he was just... sleeping...?

A flash of hatred zapped my heart, '*He* did this to me!' I hated him. I hated him. I hated him, but I felt guilty for hating him. It wasn't his fault. It was mine. I had poison for blood... I was poison... It was making me vengeful and angry and dulling my mind into one that jumped for quick fights. I took a step away from Superiorii Phorgiveness, refusing to look at his face out of fear I might start hating it, or worse, craving it, and took another step towards the door. Each step was acknowledged and accounted for.

First step. My right hip slumped into my insides. Second

step. Third step. I dropped my foot a little too hard, so my lower organs jumped and slammed down against my waist. I groaned, whipped towards Superiorii Phorgiveness, cried a little from twisting the sharp demon inside me, and watched him still sleeping. The bastard... Fourth step. Pained. I turned back around while taking it. Fifth step. Something shot out of me... It was a spitball... The Fos Terata was spitting out its evil... My head, neck, shoulders twitched from the cringe, but I moved on. I would reach the family door even if I died there. Sixth step. Seventh step. Eighth step. Ninth. All of them painless. I could feel the slob swishing between my thighs each time I moved which, to say the least, disturbed me, but there was no shock or dullness. I lifted my hand, enveloped the door handle within it, clicked it, and opened the door softly. My room was all the way down the dark hall... a good twenty steps... but I had to make it... I stole a breath and pressed a tenth, eleventh, twelve, thirteenth, fourteenth step forward. I exhaled. Not breathing helped ward off the pain while I moved, but when gathering a breath, I was flooded with more torture than before. Dizziness struck me, braiding my brains and nerves together, my eyes blanketed beneath a tub of blood, but another breath, taken a little deeper, thrusted me a fifteenth, sixteenth, seventeenth, eighteenth, nineteenth, twentieth, twenty-first step further. Stop. The darkness was a swirl. Little white spots glittered before me. The portal was opening. My sides were pinned in, my stomach squished, my body demanded relief. It was growing inside me, eating my organs. I gasped. Sparks of worry ignited. Did slumbering people hear my lungs stabbing the air? Or my thunderous footsteps? A beast clawed its talons into my ears and flailed my hearing from me. Whistling echoed violently, stealing away the little thought I managed. I lifted my unsteady head to note the distance between myself and the door. Not even half way through... I wanted to cry, but without thinking, I pushed myself forward, wrestling another step, then a twenty-third, twenty-fourth, twenty-fifth, twenty-sixth, twenty-seventh, twenty-eighth, but I thudded against the wall and every pore opened to choke on my sweat. My lower back was a sledge-hammered wall caving in, crumbling into bite-sized pieces. My ribs were pulsing. My vision so blurred, opening my eyes hurt my empty head. I only had seven or eight steps left. I took another step, sliding myself over the wall for support. My mouth opened, face twisted, nothing came out. No tears. No sound. I took another breath, held it, and took another step. I did it again and again and again and again. I only had two more steps in front of me... but I needed to breathe. The pain shortened my endurance, but I forced those last two steps without a breath in my lungs and tossed myself onto the grounds of my family's door.

I hated the floor. I hated the walls. I hated the door. I hated anything 'hard'. I hated anything 'soft'. I hated darkness. I hated my cheeks. I hated my stomach. I hated my head. I hated my legs. I hated my feet. I hated my chest. I hated Superiorii Phorgiveness. I hated my father. I hated my mother. I felt guilt over thinking about how much I hated them. I hated my guilt. I hated my feelings. I hated Superiorii Phorgiveness's wife. I really hated Superiorii Phorgiveness's wife. The thought of her dying made me a little happy, gave me a little solace, but I remembered how I hated my feelings and hated my lips for curling into a smile. They hung in a frown, shielding a moan from echoing through the halls. I hated sound. I hated anything that made noise. I hated anyone that made noise. I hated my ears. I hated my ability to hear. I hated my ability to see. I hated my ability to feel. I hated my ability to think. I hated thoughts. I hated ideas. I hated words. I hated hating so many things. I hated hating hatred and hated myself even more for having hated hatred and then thought about how hateful I was being and started hating thoughts and myself even more. I hated things that could build up. I hated the sound of shuffling feet. I hated the sound of doors creaking open. It was all so obnoxious and the mothers of those sounds should be executed swiftly. I hated death. I hated life. I hated being alive. I hated not being dead.

"Jane?" my mother rushed down towards me, took my head

up in one hand, and tilted me over to see the absence of my face. "Jane...?" she called out again, readying herself, "What happened to your forehead? What happened? Jane... It's all going to be okay soon, don't worry..." she slipped her hands beneath my right ribs, which placed even more pressure on my side, and rolled me into her arms. Like Superiorii Phorgiveness she carried me into our room and lowered me onto my father's bed... but father didn't like that.

"What are you doing?" he groaned, awaking from his comfortable slumber.

"Jane is having her first blood loss," she answered, slipping a blanket beneath me, but father whipped the sheet out of her hand which rocked the bed and my insides along with it.

"Get her off the bed!" he demanded, "She's getting blood everywhere!"

'Blood...?' I thought. The Antifasi was punishing me; he was murdering me! Bleeding! I was bleeding! Any sane person would've cried out in fear! The pain, the dizziness, the weakness, my rage were symptoms of my bleeding to death.

"Look at her, John!" my mother insisted, reaching for the blanket, "She's sweating! She's in pain! You cannot be this cruel to your own daughter!"

"She was cruel to me!" my father defended, "She embarrassed me! She betrayed my honor! And now she wants my help? She can find another father who tolerates her embarrassment, but this bed, these sheets, these are mine! And I will not have her staining them with blood- pick her up," he ordered, but my mother refused.

She pressed her curled fingers against my skull and unfolded them as she got to the base of my head, making me feel euphoric and calm. Her stare was neither euphoric nor calm, though. My father turned around and slammed himself back onto the bed, disregarding us both, though a simple recline would've sufficed, but, of course, he needed to assert his dominance. My mother stood there caressing my head for a little while longer, uncertain of what to do, but holding her breath, hoping my father would forget what he said, but he didn't. He began nudging me off the bed, his elbow pressing into my stomach which made me moan out in pain, and my mother picked me up.

"*John!*" she hissed, but he ignored her. "John!" she hissed again, louder than before.

"Do not scream at me," my father warned, whipping back around, staring my mother down and pointing his finger at her, "Never scream at me again... Is that understood?" She refused to answer. "Is that understood?" he repeated, lifting himself further off from his pillow. She continued refusing. It was the first time I'd seen my mother defy my father. "Answer me... or I'll make you understand..."

"She's your daughter, John," she informed, "That's the only thing that needs to be understood..." her voice was soft, but purposeful- like water spilling over a table. "You're pushing your sick daughter off the family bed which we both let you sleep in without a problem because-..."

"Because I'm a Superiorii and I need to have good sleep otherwise, how exactly am I supposed to protect the congregation?" It was another one of those rhetorical questions arrogant people ask to end conversations because they can't bear listening to anyone else besides themselves. My father whipped the blankets off him and stomped his way over to my mother who was cowering back against the wall behind her, "And if you have a problem with that, find another man who's willing to sacrifice his sleep for his ungrateful wife and the embarrassment he has for a daughter! Maybe Superiorii Phorgiveness will be charitable enough to help you? He's the most open hearted of the congregation! But I don't even think he wants to touch either you or Jane... And if she wasn't bleeding, I'd be more than happy to have her sleep in the family bed, but she's bleeding! *Bleeding!*" He screamed in her face, "Get that through your bald head!"

My mother then committed the ultimate impurity in my father's eyes... She cried. Her chest caved in and expanded out, bouncing me back and forth like Superiorii Phorgiveness's laughter, stirring my insides. 'Stop! Stop it! Stop crying! Why are you always crying?' was the only thought screaming through my dizzied mind along with the acknowledgment of my discomfort from feeling my mother's weak arms pressing against my ribs and thighs. I was getting blood on her wrist. My weight was probably making her spine ache. She wasn't thinking about that. She laid me on the bed instead and choked out, "We're your family, John! How can you take care of a congregation when you're cruel to your *own* family?"

"*Cruel?*" he gasped, "The only cruel person here is *you*! Cruel to me! Cruel to the Antifasi! How dare you insult me! The Antifasi has appointed me protector over his congregation and on top of this difficult assignment, I also have to protect the congregation, *including this family*, from Superiorii Faithfull's 'reforms'! The sheer *stress*," he stressed, "I've been under has been unbearable! But I continue working to keep everyone safe, including *you* and *your daughter*, but someone as *selfish* as you will never see that! All you'll ever see is what makes *you* sad! 'Oh! Poor me! My mean, old husband won't let me sleep in his bed! He won't even let our daughter sleep on his bed even though she's gushing *blood!* How *cruel!* Oh! Poor me!'" he mocked, "And then you have the audacity to cry? *Cry?*"

I hated their voices. I hated their presence. I wanted them gone. I wanted them dead. I wanted isolation. I wanted death. Everything hurt. They made it worse. They were selfish. I wanted to be selfish. They wouldn't let me be selfish because it would get in the way of them being selfish. I hated my mother. I hated my father. I wanted the bed. I wanted the blankets. I wanted Superiorii Phorgiveness.

Then something twisted inside of me. It felt both hot

and cold, a dry hand, twisting the mouth of my stomach until it burned. It was lower, in the same place all my other cramps were, but it shot up to my stomach like a shooting needle and I squirmed in bed from the pain. I tried turning on my side, but I could feel the blood dripping towards the back of my already damp potato sack dress. The pain was my puppet master, I was the Fos Terata's doll on strings, and it was tossing me around.

"Mother...!" I moaned, "*Mother...!*"

"Jane," she called, "What's wrong Jane?" her words were a dehydrated man crawling through the desert of my ears. I couldn't keep her response alive in my head. It was pushed out by another zap of pain which flipped me onto my other side. I curled up and felt someone's hands on me, most likely my mother's, but I shut my eyes, coiled myself even tighter into a little ball, and heaved out chopped up breaths from the pain. Even oxygen was making the pain worse.

"*She's getting blood on the bed!*" my father screamed, "*She's getting blood on the bed!*" Another pair of hands slammed against my side and tightened. My father was tugging at my dress, choking me with my own collar, and with every tug, rage popped in my stomach. The Fos Terata were teething at my sides now, taking their little tastes of fresh meat, instead of finishing my back and stomach off. Their venom splashed against my chest smoothly only to burn when flushed deeper into my heart. My father then ripped me towards him, away from my mother, but not out of her grip, almost throwing me off the bed where I would've cracked my head on the stone floor, and I let out a cried growl. I wanted to attack him, but I was so weak. I just wanted him to stop. I wanted to be left alone.

"*Stop it, John!*" my mother cried, "*You're hurting her!*"

"She. Is. Getting. *Blood.* On. The. *Bed!*"

My mother's nails gripped into my skin while her thumbs tightened around my arm, trying to keep me still in vain while my father continued jerking me around the bed. Her nails reminded me of the Fos Terata's hands and another cry escaped my lips and tears began streaming down my eyes from the torture.

"*You. Are. Hurting. Her. John!*" my mother screamed, "*Let her go!*"

"*Get her off the bed!*"

My lungs were filling up with heat and each pore on my forehead was kissing beads of sweat goodbye. My back, chest, and neck were moist; my inner thighs dead. The beads were ice against my hot skin and my insides were burning up, inflaming, inflating, shifting from the pain returning from my sides towards my core with a vengeance. The Fos Terata were swarming into spots all around my waist, each aiming to be the special little nuisance pummeling my stomach the most. My arms were bricks. When my father snatched me again, one of my arms slammed against my belly and I was gasping for air. When my mother pulled me back towards her, another cry broke from my lips and I felt the Fos Terata spit their poison, my blood, out of me and it oozed everywhere.

"She's getting blood *All. Over. The Bed!*" my father gasped.

"THEN LET HER!" my mother roared, but soon afterwards they both released me.

There was a beating within my ears, a pounding drum roll that sounded like my heart. I remember my father shouting abuses at my mother and my mother crying out her defenses like before, but I was slipping from reality, out of consciousness, into my mind.

'Are you okay, Jane?' Superiorii Phorgiveness asked. He was lying on the other side of the bed, facing me, petting my soaked forehead.

I shook my head in response, bringing my knees up even higher, but I was losing him. My head was so hot and dizzied it was frying my brain. All I saw around me were Fos Terata hovering over me, drool dripping from their serrated fangs, but my body swept a wave of fresh wind over my skin and revived me from my daydream. I choked out a couple sobs when I slipped back to reality because Superiorii Phorgiveness was gone, the bed was empty, and I was alone again.

While my parents screamed and cried, abused and were abused, I tried suppressing whatever feelings were trying to dribble out my stomach. Was it anger? Hatred? Depression? Rage? It felt hot. Too hot. It was churning at the mouth of my stomach and oozing higher and higher. 'No...' I swallowed, 'Don't...' I did my best to breathe normally and swallow as much as I could, but it kept rolling higher and higher and by the time it passed my frantic lungs, I knew what it was...

"*SHE'S VOMITTING ON THE BED!*" my father cried.

Yesterday's dinner was gone. It was lying there beside me on the bed, dampening my warm cheek. I had vomited out a bit of the venom, but there was still more, so I vomited a little more, and a little more, and a little more until my father hauled me off the bed, threw me onto the floor where my elbow and butt cracked against the stone, and I cried out from the pain.

"*It hurts...*" I kept moaning with specks of vomit, chunks of the charred meat, dotting my lower lip, right cheek, chin, sweat lining the sides of my face, philtrum, between my brows, and tears streaming down my cheeks, trying in vain to clean up the mess, "*It hurts... It hurts... It hurts...*"

"Stop complaining this *instant!*" my father ordered, "You are *fine!* All of this is natural and you'll do this again and again every twentieth sermon from now on, so get used to it!" he looked at the bed, the only thing that mattered, and turned back to me, "*Look at what you've done!*" he cried, "*How will your mother clean this! YOU'VE RUINED MY BED! How could you!*"

I felt someone rush towards me, wrap me in their arms, pet me, and rock me back and forth. They even kissed my sweaty forehead and brushed away the specks of slime from my lip and chin. I tried pretending it was Superiorii Phorgiveness, but she ruined the illusion. "You haven't ruined anything, Jane," she comforted, though I found it annoying because I wanted her to keep quiet, "Your father is being cruel…"

"*Cruel?*" he echoed, "No, no, no, no, *no!* I'm being understandable! Cruelty would be keeping her from marrying James before the seventh sermon because *she ruined my bed!*"

'Married…?' I thought, 'Before… the seventh sermon…' That was within the week.

"Forcing her to get married would only *add* onto to your cruelty!" she pressed my head against her chest and held me tighter within her embrace. I was probably bleeding on her again, "She can't-…" my mother choked out, but she cried again before finishing whatever she was going to say, hiding her eyes behind my scalp.

"She has to get married!" my father exasperated, "That's what the Antifasi demands! Once a girl has her first blood loss, she needs to be married before the seventh sermon otherwise she will die childless! Do you want her to be worthless?"

"*She's too young!*" my mother sobbed.

"*You were her age when we got married* and you were only a little older when I impregnated you!"

"*And I lost it because I was too young!*" my mother cried.

"You lost it because the Antifasi cursed you for keeping your first blood loss a secret for four sermons," my father corrected, "She will not suffer the same fate. I will make sure of it."

And with that, nothing else was said. My father tore off the blankets from the bed, getting a little bile on his chest which he screamed at, stomped towards the opposite corner of the room, tossed the blankets there, rushed back towards the bed where he pulled our wash basin from beneath, and stormed out of the room. My mother was holding me close to her, but it was to keep herself stable and whole. She supported the back of my head with one of her palms, but her grip around my body

145

was too tight. It was pushing my organs inwards and squeezing more of the venom out of me, so I pushed her away from me, but she clung onto me. After I showed more struggle, she let me go and I rolled onto the ground where I curled back up again, wrapping my arms around myself, pretending they were Superiorii Phorgiveness's arms. My mother stayed sitting where she was and that's how we remained.

"I'm so sorry, Jane," she whimpered, "I wish I had been braver..."

C hapter Eleven

Nothing special was arranged for the wedding. Unlike your world, the bride doesn't wear a beautiful dress, face full of colors, and doesn't walk down the aisle to meet her handsome tear-stricken groom waiting for her at the end. The groom is neutral and dutiful. Excitement mustn't show on his face otherwise it would be misconstrued, or rightfully interpreted, as him growing excited for what comes after the ceremony. It indicated his depravity and hidden immorality. Since James was going to be a future Superiorii through marriage, he had to look especially indifferent towards me. However, despite knowing what should and should not be done on the groom's part, I couldn't help, but think his indifference, borderline disappointment with me, was genuine.

For my part, I was wearing the congregation's famous tattered, soiled, potato sack dress which covered my entire body, a disgusting garb reserved for every bride to wear. It was covered with dry patches of blood from past brides who were, of course, on their time of the month, plus my fresh stains. I wore another potato sack over my head with two holes cut out for my eyes. The visible area around my eyes were powdered with ash from the furnace room to further mask my impurities as a woman.

From my first blood loss to my wedding day, I was imprisoned within the family room, so no man was tempted by my womanly, unclaimed flesh. I was now an unmarried, virginal woman. The temptation for action, let alone impure thoughts, against me would've been too strong for grown men to control. I would've been put to death, with the Superiorii's allowance, by the jealous wives of the congregation for my having tampered and torn their union to grown men beneath the Antifasi. That's why every centimeter of my skin had to be covered on my wedding day. If even an inch showed, I would've been dragged and burned for my whoredom.

I was married on the fourth day of my blood loss. My father administered my matrimonial sermon. I was seated in the front row beside my mother, as usual, while my father lectured about the sanctity of marriage, the severity of our vows, and the union between our lives until death came between us. James would be my leader. My head. I was expected to be his helper and bear his child, specifically a son, so his bloodline as Superiorii could continue and the congregation would run smoothly. I was expected to keep away from every brother to secure the safety of my reputation as a loyal wife to my husband. If neither my husband nor other sisters were present and a brother came near, I was expected to scurry away. I was expected to keep quiet in public to save James from humiliation. I was expected to obey him in accordance with the Antifasi's laws. Any deviance marked me an outsider. I would be shunned until I changed my ways; hence why most women, except for women like Aunt Faithfull and Jeanette who held influence, kept quiet.

James was supposed to take care of me and his future child, a son, spiritually. He was supposed to keep the congregation and his family clean and chaste. Any sign of impurity within his family or the congregation rested on his shoulders as Superiorii and he was supposed to handle it swiftly otherwise be stripped of his title. Any sign of impurity within his family would not only deem him an inept Superiorii, but also a weak, foolish, and impure man. Unlike women, though, once a man was considered weak, foolish, and impure, the shunning would never end. He would forever be considered a man without character.

Once father was done stating the obvious, James stood up from his usual seat, leaving his parents behind, and walked onto the platform, taking his seat in the only chair provided. After he sat down, my father looked at me, along with the congregation, and my mother gently nudged me to get up, so I did. I walked towards the platform, took care with stepping onto it, so I didn't trip over the long potato sack dress, walked over to James, and sat at his feet about a foot away from him. He refused to look at me, but I couldn't help but look at him. His messy, disheveled, blonde hair. His brown eyes, red where they were supposed to be white, purposely avoiding me. Even the chair seemed uncomfortable to him. He was so unlike Superiorii Phorgiveness. If anyone had the right to be disappointed, it should've been me. I scowled at him, gritted my teeth, and allowed hatred to carve its print into my stare regardless of the tears that might flow beneath my headdress. In the end, I was glad I had something covering my face. They could force me to marry someone I didn't love, but they couldn't force me to hide my feelings- not when they couldn't see them.

"James..." my father called to which James stood up from his chair with perfect posture, "... will you devote your life to keeping the congregation clean from the Fos Terata's influence, making sure it lives by the Antifasi's standards?"

He nodded and said, "Yes." The congregation applauded and then calmed.

"James..." my father called again, "... will you spend night and day worrying about the congregation, thinking of everything that could be wrong with it? Will you fill your days with helping those in need of correction and your nights with reading from the Den Amfisvito?"

He nodded and said, "Yes." The congregation applauded and then calmed.

"James..." my father called a third time, "... will you devote your life to keeping your wife and future child clean from the Fos Terata's influence, making sure they live according to the Antifasi's standards?"

He nodded and said, "Yes." The congregation applauded and then calmed.

"James..." my father called for the last time, "... will you spend night and day worrying about your family, thinking about everything that could be wrong with them? Will you fill your days with correcting your wife and child and your nights with chastity after your child is born?"

He nodded and said, "Yes." The congregation applauded and then calmed.

"Very well, James..." my father said, "... you may sit down now." James obeyed.

"Jane..." my father called to which I stood up, walked towards the spot behind James's seat, and stood there huddled over myself. My father was looking me in the eye, but I was staring at his knees, "... will you obey, support, and promise your silence to James as his wife and as the wife of a Superiorii?"

Up until that point, I had been going through the motions. I was playing their game and abiding by their rules. I did, from time to time, imagine Superiorii Phorgiveness sitting in James's place. Although, if Superiorii Phorgiveness had been in James's place, he would've picked me off the ground, taken the bag off my head, brushed away the ash from my eyes, and smiled at me. The reality of my getting married didn't sink in until my father used the word wife at me. That word was reserved for my mother or other married women, but never had I imagined myself being called 'wife'. I still can't. The label carries the weight of adulthood, motherhood, and responsibility and I couldn't imagine any of those labels describing me either. I was just Jane. And I was just a child.

My gaze turned from my father towards the second row where my mother was sitting. It was the farthest I could look to the left without turning my head. I wanted Superiorii Phorgivenss. I knew he was in the crowd. I knew he was watching me, but I didn't know what he thought about me being married off... I didn't know what he was feeling. We hadn't seen each other since I bled on him, four days ago, and now, he sees me, this child he would spend his nights with, dressed from head to toe, as a woman, getting married. If I hadn't been so weak, I would've confessed my love for Superiorii Phorgiveness, he would've confessed his love for me, and we would've locked ourselves in that room in which no one would've found us. We would've lived off our imagination, had a child, and raised him or her within our world.

"Jane...?" my father called, sternly. I flinched my gaze back towards him, paying him the full attention he wanted, as he repeated himself, "... will you obey, support, and promise your silence to James as his wife and as the wife of a Superiorii?"

I nodded and said, "Yes." The congregation applauded, but hesitantly. I had taken too long. I was clearly thinking before answering.

"Jane..." my father called a second time, "... will you fulfill your nightly duties as wife, and as wife to a member of the Superiorii, by lying with your husband until a healthy child is conceived? Will you do your best to give birth to a son?"

I nodded and said, "Yes." The congregation applauded like they had with James.

"Jane..." my father called for a third time. Anxiety warmed my neck and collarbone as I neared the end of my vows. I didn't want to say yes. I didn't want to get married. I didn't want to sleep with James. I didn't want to get pregnant. I didn't want to give birth. I didn't want to be a mother. I didn't want to be an adult. I just wanted to be with Superiorii Phorgiveness. I looked down at James, looking at the grease and white specks in his hair which was common within the underground, and imagined dark hair before me. "Jane keep looking at me- don't look down- keep looking at me, Jane," my father demanded. I looked back up at him, noticed his eyes widening and his nostrils flaring, and grew scared about what he'd say or do to me once all this was over and we were back in the family room again, but then it hit me. I wasn't going back to the family room. I was moving into another room. My new room. The room I'd give birth in, grow old in, and die in. That would be my home now. I would never be alone with my parents again. It was a harsh reality change, but also an exciting one. "... will you uphold a conduct befitting a wife of the Superiorii and a sister of the congregation? Will you refrain from idle gossip, maintain a good reputation, and keep your silence while your husband speaks?"

I nodded and said, "Yes." The congregation applauded and then calmed.

"Jane..." my father called for the last time, "... will you raise your child to love and follow the Antifasi's laws? Will you raise your child to be an honorable member of the congregation as the mother to a future Superiorii?"

I nodded and said, "Yes." The congregation applauded and then calmed.

"Very well, Jane..." my father said, "... you may sit down now." Which I did. I walked around James, back over to my spot on the floor before his feet, and stared at them. I imagined the obvious. In my mind, I was sitting at Superiorii Phorgiveness's feet.

"Now that the congregation has witnessed the marriage between James and Jane, let it be known... James will become Superiorii one day and must live up to the heightened expectations all members of the Superiorii must live up to in order to give the congregation an example of purity. And Jane will one day birth a son which will carry on the Superiorii lineage," my father announced which overcame me with dread again.

The congregation applauded and then calmed.

"We shall now begin the morning's sermon," and with that, I was married. There was no reception, no celebration, no congratulation. The entire affair was a matter of duty and only worse was to come. I couldn't stop thinking of what was going to happen that night between us and what would continue happening until I finally gave birth to a healthy child. It was a disgusting, impure act, but it was one that we had to perform. A dirty, regrettable responsibility fulfilled by confused, passive-aggressive people.

Both James and I awkwardly stood up, trying to get off the platform as quickly as possible because the longer we stayed, the more it seemed we were vying for the congregation's attention, but I, unfortunately, stood up so quickly I lost my balance. My knees wobbled beneath me, my ankles weakened, and when I took a step back, I tripped over my tattered, bloodied dress and dropped hard against the floor near my father. I grunted and then whimpered at the blow my body, and specifically the corner of my elbow, took from the stone floor, but when I opened my eyes up to the ceiling, I noticed my father's snarling face returning towards the congregation.

Part of me hoped either he or even James would help me up, but neither did. Father continued addressing the congregation, lecturing them on the importance of obedience, and James was already sitting in our row. By the time I stood up, fully embarrassed, but fully indifferent all the same, the scratch of not being cared about itched its way down my throat and I swallowed it. My hurt feelings were my fault. I had placed an unrealistic expectation on people who only cared about themselves or were oblivious. I ignored the congregation, probably looking at me rather than my father since I was more of an interesting spectacle, and walked towards my seat imagining their judgmental eyes beading at me. I was, at best, a fool, but most of them probably thought I was a bride desperate for attention...

... and to a degree, they weren't wrong in either case.

After the sermon concluded, dinner was served. Rotten potatoes, bread, and water per usual. My family and James's sat together for dinner, quietly, with our parents sitting on one side and James and I sitting on the other at a distance from one another. We tried not looking up from our plates, let alone looking at one another, but I couldn't help swiping glimpses at everyone. I started from the farthest corner from me and then fanned down the line where my mother sat. As I chewed my rock hard, stale bread, I looked at James's mother. She was sitting hunched over her plate, pecking at her food bit by bit, but still managing to finish the meal. James had blonde hair because of her. There was no shadow of growing hair on her head. She looked completely bald because of its fairness. She was a skinny woman, as was everyone, but the bones protruding from her face only served to better emphasize this empty stare she had. Was there even a point to her life? She didn't seem like a woman with depth, or even interests, like everyone else in the congregation, but she especially seemed content with nothing. It wasn't a humble position to take. She wasn't a monk appreciating the little things in life, she had no life in her. No personality. She was bland. And she was my mother-in-law... She gave birth to my husband...

Her husband, my father-in-law, was the male version of her. His gaze wasn't completely empty. It was a wall. It wasn't angry. It was harsh. Scolding. Disciplinary. He was a man with a hard countenance. His hair was brown, hacked up, and he was balding. His hairline wasn't receding and there wasn't a bald patch at the back of his head either. There were bald patches spotting random parts of his head. He probably had a sort of scalp infection. I didn't know how exactly James arranged their room and who got to sleep where, but I now know neither James nor his mother slept with him. He could've slept on the floor or the bed, but they were sleeping where he wasn't. It was also apparent that the man was hardly touched if at all. No embraces. No hugs. Nothing. How do I know this? He had ringworm on different patches of his skin, and who knows where else, so if they slept in the same bed or touched him, they would've both been infected, but neither were. Thus, I wasn't infected either.

I had swallowed the last morsel of my hard bread when I swept a quick glance over at my father and began chewing, to the best of my ability, my rotten potatoes. It was beyond mushy, I could've drunk it, and there were little thick, wiry bits within it, and every now and then I would feel one of those sprouts tickle against my tongue. I would've made a face, but I learned not to make faces at my food when I was little. The food was generously given to us from the Antifasi, so it had to be the most delicious meal to us otherwise we were ungrateful.

'But if the Antifasi is so loving, powerful, and generous, why couldn't he give us better food?' I always wondered, but as soon as the question crossed my mind, my brows quivered from the guilt. My mind immediately reasoned the congregation was impure and undeserving. The Antifasi giving us these life sustaining meals was more than we deserved because we were ungrateful, dirty cretins who deserved death. I was just one more example proving how truly spoiled we were.

The little glimpse I swiped at my father was enough for me to tell he was reeling back from his rage. He was trying to control himself again. I had further embarrassed him, but the good thing was I no longer lived with him anymore. He got his wish. I was no longer his daughter, but a wife to another man. My conduct no longer reflected on my father's upbringing, but my husband's management, so father had to take his rage out on my mother from now on.

I swallowed all the slimy, watery chunks of potato as fast and as inconspicuous as I could and reached for my glass of water, trying to look at my mother without getting noticed. She was looking down at her unfinished plate. Her glass was full. As warm water cleansed my throat from all the gunk left behind by the potato, I continued watching my mother, trying to read what she was thinking. What does she think about me being married? I think she wants me to get pregnant because that's my responsibility, it's the right thing to do, but why hasn't she told me anything about being a mother? Is this how mothers react to their daughters getting married? I mean, James's parents also weren't reacting, but my mother wasn't like his. There was something more to my mother, but probably not much more.

James's father was the first to look up from his plate, or whatever spot on the table he chose to look at throughout the meal. He swept a look over everyone's plates and noticed most of them empty and my father, soon doing the same thing, spoke first, "James..." he addressed, "... do you know what to do?" he nodded.

"I taught him exactly what to do, what might happen, and how to handle it, Superiorii Loyaltie," James's father assured.

"Good," my father swallowed, nodding his head as confirmation that he was pleased with Brother Virtew's preparation.

I was waiting for someone to tell me what was going on or at the very least acknowledge me, but no one did. Not even my mother. She just continued looking at her plate, holding onto her fork tightly, so tightly her skin was white, and her lips were now curling in. She wanted to cry. I could tell. I felt the pressure of a question pushing itself against my teeth, urging my lips to part to make it easier for it to escape, and when my lips parted, the tip of my tongue rose, but my mind muted me.

"I think it's time, James..." my father announced, looking at him in expectation along with Brother Virtew. James then stood up and waited behind his chair, looking at the empty plate before me, but not looking at me. Was he thinking about something? Did he need to study the Den Amfisvito now? When I looked away from him, I noticed everyone looking at me. They had the same expectation in their eyes, but it was much more forceful. I think they thought I was going to resist. As if something bad was going to happen to me, but they were going to push me into it anyways. The good thing, though, was my ignorance. The bad thing was also my ignorance. It was a double-edged sword.

"Do I get up, too?" I asked, which only further revealed my own stupidity.

"Yes, Jane," my father answered with a, 'What else do you think we want you to do?' caught in his throat.

"Oh... okay..." I said, standing up. I glanced over at my mother once, but she was still clenching her fork, breathing hard. "What do I do now...?"

"James already knows what to do, so wait for him to tell you and listen to whatever he says," my father answered, turning his stare back towards James, "Are you ready...?" he asked. James nodded his head again and with that my father said, "Good... The two of you may now leave."

Leave? Were we going to our new room? I thought that was happening later, once all the families adjourned back to their rooms. James didn't look at me. He walked off without me, not even checking if I was following him. I looked back at my father as if I had misheard everything, but the anger in his eyes kept growing until his nostrils started batting out with a fury, so I left. I followed James into the same hallway my family and I slept in, happy I still had my room in the hall opposite the left furnace room. It was three doors down from my old room, though. I didn't like the distance because I thought I'd be farther away from my father, but at least I wasn't in the same room with him anymore. I never had to be stuck in private with him again. He would never scream at me or pound his fists around me. I was free.

James pushed the door open, walked in, and I followed.

"Close the door," he said, so I did. So far, so good.

He then stood in silence within the room, most likely meditating on the Antifasi. He stood there with his eyes closed and head bowed. Was I supposed to be meditating, too?

Afterwards, he looked up, not saying or doing anything for a little while, and then took a deep breath. He held it, lifted his potato sack dress, removed his underwear, and then exhaled.

"Do the same," he said, but I hesitated. I didn't feel comfortable undressing before him. "Are you refusing to listen to me, woman?" he snapped, whipping his arm in my direction with more expression than I'd seen the entire day.

I shook my head quickly and choked out a, "No," through my shock. I bent over, rolled my long dress up to my upper thighs, and reached for my underwear, pulling them down, and kicking them away. He wasn't looking at me anymore. He stopped looking at me after I bent down.

"Get on the bed," he said, so I did. I took a seat there.

"You're not supposed to sit there!" he moaned, sighing out his frustrations, "*Lie down...!*"

"Oh... okay..." I said, quickly turning myself around, throwing my legs on the bed, my back against the wall, and sliding further and further down until I was completely flat on my back.

"Close your eyes," he said, so I did. How long did I have to keep them closed for, though?

The question jumped out of my mind once I heard his feet brushing closer and closer to me. His breath was getting harder. He sounded like a dying man. I wanted to ask him if he was alright, help him if I could, but I knew my concern would've served to annoy him more than help him. Once he was close enough, he pressed a knee onto the bed and climbed over my legs, adjusting himself soon after by pressing one knee on my right side and another over my left. He rolled my dress back up to my upper thighs, making sure it went no higher, and lowered himself onto me. He was sitting, bare, on my legs and I soon felt a giggle crawling up my lungs. I did my best not to laugh, but it was so weird. Some young man I've known for years now had his testicles on my legs. I was also very uncomfortable with my dress now high enough for him to pull a little higher and see something I didn't want him to see. It was so weird... so I laughed... and he smacked me across the face.

"Don't you ever laugh at me!" he ordered, "You will never laugh at me, is that understood?" I nodded, but now I couldn't help myself from crying. It hurt. He really hurt me. *"Crying?"* he scorned, *"You're such a child..."* 'What is going on?' was all I could think of, "Open your legs wider," James demanded. James pressed his palms against my thighs and flung them apart. He threw himself down against me and started moving harshly, but I didn't know exactly what he was trying to do... until he did it.

I screamed, he was ripping me apart, tearing my vagina like a dress, stabbing me over and over and over, but he kept going, muffling my mouth. Once. Twice. Three times. Four. And with a grunt, he was done.

When he rolled himself off me, I curled up to my side, facing away from him, crying out in fear and agony, immediately checking for any blood gushing out of me- any rips or tears. My menstruation had reached a point where I was just spotting, so if there was any blood gushing down my leg, it was because of James and I needed help. But there wasn't as much blood as I would've thought there would've been for the pain caused. My vagina felt burning hot and I'm sure a doctor would've noted some tears and internal damage, but I brushed away my pain because I was used to sweeping my feelings, whether physical or emotional, aside. However, I did find slime where the blood was coming out... and in disgust... I tried scooping it out. But, before I could finish, James grabbed me.

"Stop!" he said, so I did, "That's what gets you pregnant! Now we'll have to do this all over again!"

"I'm sorry..." I said, "... I didn't know..."

"You don't know anything!" he slammed, "You were an embarrassment to your father and you'll be a humiliation to me!" He pierced my heart with the sharpest of words, "You better know how to have a son otherwise you're going to have many dead daughters, Jane..." he warned.

"What...?" I gasped.

"I. Want. A. Son," he reiterated.

"How can you say something like that...?" my heart sunk. I was married to a psychopath... He was going to kill me... "Are you saying *you're* going to kill our daughters, James?"

"That's what you do when your wife doesn't understand her role to give birth to a son," he informed, "You punish her."

"No..." I gasped, shaking my head, "... no... no! No! You're a monster!" I started screaming, "You're an evil monster!" I turned back over and started ripping the slime from me, I couldn't get pregnant with this monster's child, but he threw me back over, flat on my back, grabbed my wrists, and rushed his face closer to mine.

"That's what you do, Jane!" he barked, "That's what all Superiorii have done since the dawn of time! Your father and Superiorii Phorgiveness are the only exceptions and now I have to put up with a stupid child just like Juliet's husband has to put up with her!"

"That's not true! That's not true!" I screamed, "It's evil! It's too evil! How could the Antifasi allow the Superiorii to do this? They can't..." I cried.

"The Antifasi said it was shameful for a Superiorii to have a daughter in the Den Amfisvito... If you were born a boy, you would've known that... That's why he allowed the Superiorii to smother their daughters... Otherwise," he explained, severely, but not sacrificing himself totally to his heated hatred, "how could we be fully respected? Juliet is the reason why Superiorii Phorgivenss can't give sermons and you're the reason your father can be publicly questioned! But they deserve their disrespect for being too weak to kill you two! The two of you are curses on your families, but I will not tolerate a curse upon ours!"

I couldn't say anything. I was in shock. Questions were running wild, beating against my skull with such fury I could feel my veins pulsing within my forehead. I pressed my lips together as hard as I could, trying not to cry out, and with that,

James seemed satisfied. As long as I didn't make too much noise, I was alright. So, I closed my eyes, rolled myself back up into a sitting position, brought my feet closer to myself, but before I could raise the blankets, James said, "You sleep on the floor," so I did. I climbed off the bed, walked over to a corner of the room like my mother did, and slept there, crying myself silently to sleep.

C hapter Twelve

After two months of marriage, the Aunts, including my mother, deemed me pregnant. James was banned from touching me until a healthy baby was born and went so far as to let me sleep in the family bed, so I felt more inclined to give birth to his son. As if I could choose to withhold a son from him.

Before the congregation's eyes, I stood by James's side silently, the accessory to his dominance, bolstering his image. Yes, I am subservient. Yes, I am obedient. Yes, James puts me in my place. He disciplines me well. He would make a great member of the Superiorii. He demands obedience and disciplines people proportionate to their actions. He doesn't tolerate insubordination. Won't you accept him as your leader like I have? It was disgusting. I hated him. When I felt sparkles of gratitude towards him for letting me sleep in our bed, acknowledging my existence, talking to me, I hated him even more. How degraded had I become to feel appreciative towards someone treating me relatively well? How warped had my views become that being allowed to sleep in a bed, whilst pregnant no less, was a gracious act?

At night, I'd climb onto my side of the bed, the side pressed against the wall because James, in his kind consideration, wanted to block me from falling off the other side. I'd crowd the wall to keep from feeling his warmth. He was a steaming pile of shit to me. The worst part came after the congregation broke up and the members retired to their rooms while the Superiorii and their successors rejoined in their little 'office' for further study and conversation. They needed to talk about topics for sermons and whether or not anyone detected impurity among the members. This wasn't problematic for me because it meant I had the room to myself for a while.

I didn't have to fake thoughts or feelings, at least for a little while, because no one was around quizzing my every detail. I went to bed early, though. Sleeping had become my refuge from the world. When once I tried staying awake all night for Superiorii Phorgiveness, I now tried sleeping my life away to hide from everyone else. My dreams, though growing more and more disturbed with images of organs and knives and blood and skin stamping every alternate reality I conjured, were far better than the reality I was living. James didn't care about my rest. He liked rubbing my face in his authority. This is where the worst part comes in.

Every night, as I took my final steps into my subconscious, falling peacefully asleep, James would barge in, not caring for the slamming of the door, and talk to me. I had to endure his constant yammering about Superiorii business, the grunts he vocalized as he removed his potato sack outfit through the stress of the day, and the thud of his corpse against the bed, bouncing me a millimeter off the mattress. Every time I heard the door slam, my heart turned to boiling clay. I hated his excitement. I knew his positive expression would turn equally negative if I displeased him, especially in failing at giving birth to a son. He was a spoiled child.

I was always so close... only a few moments more and I would've lost myself in my subconscious. James pounding the door open would've been inconsequential. I wouldn't hear him yammer on about nonsense. I wouldn't notice him bouncing me from the bed. He wouldn't give me the satisfaction... He had to rip me from my dreams... He had to possess me every second.

The more he spoke, the hotter my heart grew. It melted over my lungs and into my stomach, weighing my chest down with its heavy matter. The mass cooled over my lungs, solidifying them in place, keeping them from expanding to allow me one good breath. I drowned during his barraging. My stomach churned the rolling, boiling clay swirling within its acid, burning me from the inside out. You could only imagine the effect being popped off the bed had when all this internal mayhem was going on. 'Stop talking, stop talking, stop talking, stop talking,' and once the jump came, *'I'll kill you!'* but I was impaled with guilt at this slip. Hatred poisons humanity and my feelings were being murdered. I loathed James. I wanted him dead. I was taking baby steps towards not caring if it was wrong to dream about his murder. The Antifasi wasn't married to him. I was. If he wanted me to respect James, he could come down, marry him, and prove such an attitude was possible. Until then, I was going to dream all I wanted. However, in my conscious life, I would continue feeling guilt.

There was an advantage to James's incessant gossip, however. The silver lining to my dark cloud. At times, and ignorantly so, he would trek over Superiorii Phorgiveness's name and tell me what he did or said. James brought him up as a minor detail in his gossip considering Superiorii Phorgiveness's reserved character, but hearing his name was enough to spark my happiness. I missed him. Since my first blood loss, I hadn't once spoken to him or even geared a shared look towards him. I caught glimpses of his face whenever I could during sermons, but each time he felt eyes on him, he looked in my direction and I flinched away. I pretended to pay placid attention to the sermon being administered and, at times, with full regret, ignored his prolonged stares. He was trying to catch my attention, but was it to mock me? To tell me he knew I had been looking? Or because he missed me, too? The latter was an impossible and far too idealistic notion, so I believed in the former instead. I was a joke to him. The girl who bled on him and ran. That's what my existence meant to him now. He probably even forgot my name.

I indulged the impure thoughts I had about him whether or not I was looking at him, though. None of it was sexual. The limited experience I had with sex was a confusing horror. He's hurting me! But, is he really hurting me? He's ripping me apart! Has anything been cut or torn? Has he hurt me? Shouldn't I be bleeding? What did he do to me? These questions plagued me until the Aunts granted me my temporary freedom.

My impure thoughts involved Superiorii Phorgiveness sitting in James's place, going to bed with me, holding me, telling me he loved me, making sure I wasn't sad or alone, brushing my hair when I cried, even just looking at me with warmth. And I felt guilty over these thoughts because he wasn't my husband. Life had deprived me of love and I hated it for it, but the guilt of hating life remained. I wanted Superiorii Phorgiveness to be the father of my child, not James. Guilt. I wanted to go to sleep and never wake up. Guilt. I wanted someone who actually loved me. Guilt.

Guilt made a person whole. If someone lacked guilt, they were not members of the congregation, but portals for the Fos Terata. The congregation considered guilt a nutritious meal and fed it to their babies, so they grew up weak and fragile. Every rational thought I had was undermined by guilt. Every reasonable feeling was laughed at by guilt. Guilt was the demon whispering in my ear, "Everything you do is wrong... You're a burden to others... You're an evil that needs to be cleansed."

Every time I looked down at my belly, I wanted Superiorii Phorgivness's child, not James's, and every time the thought passed, a pang of guilt riveted down my spine. The child was guilt. It was a ball of guilt poisoning me from the inside. James had injected me with guilt to control me from within.

The thought of taking one of those soiled knives and cutting out the bastard child within me during dinner satisfied me. Shoving it in my stomach and slicing up whatever slime James left was comforting. The hope of it dying within me, rotting, sliding out into one decrepit ball of waste, and throwing it in James's face was delicious. This is your child, James. This is what you did to me. This is what you put inside of me. Him breaking down in front of me over the corpse of his possible son, screaming in agony like I had when he shot the bastard inside me, was electrifying. He would crumple up and sob away his never-ending sorrow in silence while I ignored his pain like he had ignored mine. Doubtless, however, I felt guilty over these little comforts as well.

Was I a woman or was I guilt incarnate?

I thought about so many things during sleepless nights, I forgot I even had a body. The only thing that existed those nights was my mind rattling against my skull like a prisoner rattling against its cage, hoping for freedom. How come I had to feel guilty over everything? James clearly wasn't guilty when he raped me time and time again through my tears. He even muffled my anguish with his hand. It annoyed him. He hurt me and he knew he was hurting me, but I didn't see the slightest shred of remorse from him. Same thing with my father. He insulted and threatened violence against his family countless times, yet never once did I see the same look in his eyes, I knew everyone saw in mine. Mourning. Regret. Hollowness. Confusion. Fear. Everyone knew I was miserable. They all claimed to help those in the congregation who needed their help, but no one gave me their shoulder. No one helped me- let alone those who claimed to be the most helpful. They ignored or criticized me. Their form of helping others was pointing out what was wrong with them and shaming them until they changed.

How come I had to feel guilty over thinking and the congregation didn't have to feel guilty over gossiping? Even James, the successor to a member of the Superiorii, excessively indulged in gossiping when he was supposed to be a tomb about Superiorii business. I wasn't supposed to know what was happening in the congregation. That was a matter for the Superiorii and the Superiorii alone, yet he felt more than inclined to tell me every detail of their interaction and pepper his own opinion over the retelling. If the Antifasi was consistent, James would be a portal for corrupting the innocent mind of his wife, telling her truths she shouldn't hear for being both a member of the congregation and a woman. There was never mention of this, though. Sermons always concerned obedience and controlling one's own thoughts, but hardly did it ever discuss controlling one's tongue. I guess the Antifasi cares more about us being obedient to him than being kind to one another.

That last thought dropped my heart. The Antifasi had given me everything. He was so kind. So good. How dare I question him? It was the brick wall I crashed into since I developed awareness... but it was slowly being corroded away by my nightly poison. One night, maybe a week or so after my pregnancy was announced, I realized I could get around the wall. I could climb over it or walk around it, but there were ways of getting around the wall. Instead of ceasing my thought process, I pushed through the Antifasi and marched forward. I didn't feel guilty for thinking when no one else felt guilty for judging, especially thoughtlessly. It was a realization that sparked a chain of events. It was my first baby step. No matter how small it was to outsiders who were encouraged to think for themselves since birth, I knew and felt it was a big and exciting step for me. I could think. And I could think without feeling wrong... at least on a few matters.

I felt comfortable thinking about my loneliness and misery. I could think about the cruelty of marriage and its potential for synthesizing two loving individuals. I could think about the Antifasi's and Superiroii's fallacies and how aspects of the congregation could be improved. I accepted I would never be understood, let alone liked for my unfiltered character, with a good helping of bitterness, but I couldn't accept the unearned feeling that came with thinking differently. I felt like I was wrong not only in opinion, but in existence. However, how could I feel wrong when Jeanette felt right?

Jeanette sat next to me and talked to me after sermons, but her presence made me lonelier. I slept with James, but his presence only made me lonelier. Loneliness isn't a matter of being alone, but feeling alone. Before I was married, I didn't have friends. My parents, particularly my father, did an excellent job assuring me I was alone. However, I had Superiorii

Phorgiveness. When I didn't have him in person, I felt him in my heart. He always kept me company and supported me. He understood me. Not totally, but he understood enough. He protected me tenderly like a father supporting his baby girl.

I couldn't feel him anymore. He no longer kept me company or supported me. I had lost the privilege. The emptiness his departure left made the numbing touch of loneliness freeze against my skin. My mind remembered the feel of companionship, but my heart forgot the feeling. When your loud heart forgets peace while your quiet mind roughly remembers the path, it's a civil war which tears your identity apart.

In fact, it wasn't just the hollowness which affected me, but the confusion that accompanies it. My disintegration was an industrial nail hammered between my ribs. My sole purpose was ripping it out regardless of disfigurement. Even if there were long-lasting repercussions, during my wayward pre-adolescence- nothing was too big a sacrifice if I got rid of the pain. I needed someone to take it from me. Just one person. Another guiltless thought I indulged in was imagining intimate scenes of venting, sobbing, and being held by different members of the congregation. I imagined Juliet holding me and petting my head. In fact, she was probably the person I imagined most. I wanted to laugh with her and rant about our husbands and pet her head like she would mine. She was the closest I could get to her father.

During several sermons, I often skated my eyes over her. The possibility of her being my confidant fascinated me and I lived out my hopes while watching her. Granted, I wasn't in love with her. I was strongly infatuated with her, whether or not it was romantic was inconsequential, but I wasn't in love with her. Love is loyal, selfless, devoted, respectful of individuality, and grounded in reality. I was using her to make me feel better. I was fabricating a reality and ascribing personality traits to her I knew she didn't possess. If someone else came along and paid me a little attention, I would've given them, instead of her, my undivided attention. Imagination hybridized by attention was a fickle need, but it kept me from drowning in melancholy.

At night, I fell asleep imagining Juliet caring for me, or anyone who paid me a little positive attention throughout the day. Juliet, Janice, even Jeanette... I must confess I found myself attracted even to Jeanette with all her putrid glory. Her arrogance softened into strength when looked through the rose-tinted glasses of desperation. Her cruelty melted into care. The foul smell became her little trademark. It's not my proudest moment, but this is the reductive power of helplessness. My feelings were volatile and in need of a rock. Everyone looked emotionally more stable than me and I aspired to claim their peace, but they made me feel worse. I tried tying my problems to their rock, but they added their stones onto my weight.

"What was it like being pregnant for you, Jeanette?" I asked, turning to her after one sermon finished with my prepared question.

"It was the most spiritual time, Jane," she answered, "It was the *happiest* time of my life. I was gifted by the Antifasi! I felt deep gratitude towards my husband for doing his part in getting me pregnant. I miss being pregnant, but being a mother to a future member of the Superiorii is a gift! Why do you ask? Don't you love being pregnant?"

Of course, I didn't.

"Yes," I answered, nodding to further emphasize my lie. I wasn't guilty about lying to certain people anymore. I could lie to James or any member of the congregation and not bat an eye. "I thank the Antifasi and my husband every day for this gift..." My stomach dropped when I remembered how James jumped me, thrusted into me, silenced me, and pushed me off the bed in a sobbing heap... It was every single night for two months... Anxiety flooded me, but Jeanette, not being the wiser, brushed my flushing face away as nothing more than pregnancy symptoms.

"Being pregnant can sometimes take such a toll on you physically," 'Sometimes?' I thought, but I didn't say anything. I was fighting off the urge to vomit or cry. "You should really sit down," she insisted, but it wasn't out of concern. She wanted to get away. By the time I sat down, she had walked away, looking for someone else. If I wanted to socialize with her, she ran away, but if I pushed her away, she clung onto me furiously. Jeanette wanted what she couldn't have and stepped over what she could possess. I sat there, reminded of my loneliness, fully conscious of my pregnancy.

Jeanette was a terrible character, but she didn't compare to James and his incessant gossiping. He would tell me every detail of the congregation: who was being watched, who he thought should be watched, possible portals, and secrets confessed to members of the Superiorii, hoping for forgiveness and/or guidance. And here James was, telling me, Jane, who could've so easily had a tongue as long as Jeanette's, everything about everything I wasn't supposed to know.

"Then your father said Superiorii Faithfull's goals went against the Den Amfisvito and not only that! But he told him he should start reading the Den Amfisvito more to learn a thing or two about what the Antifasi wants! Can you believe that?"

I stayed immobile in bed, the way I had before his intrusion, facing the wall, waiting for him to grow tired of his own voice. "And then," "and then," "and then," "and then," pathetic. He sounded like an excited child telling his mother what happened at school, but his excitement was born from malice rather than innocence.

However, as I've said before, my ears reflexively pricked up whenever I heard, "Superiorii Phorgiveness," and my attention was completely his, "tried taking your father to the side to whisper some news in his ear, but Superiorii Faithfull demanded to know what was being said. Superiorii Phorgiveness obviously couldn't lie, so Superiorii Phorgiveness went up to Superiorii Faithfull and your father followed and Superiorii

THE LIGHT WAS GOOD

Depherence walked up to the group and the four of them talked amongst themselves, so I watched the Superiorii the entire time," Of course you did, James. Of course, you did. "And I saw their reactions... Superiorii Faithfull's eyes grew wide, your father's mouth dropped, but he didn't say anything. He just looked at something on the floor."

"Was the spot on the floor close to Superiorii Faithfull?" I asked, knowing my father refused to look a man in the eyes when incensed. Emotion was weakness to him after all.

"No?" James curtly answered. Pardon my interrupting your loud monologue, my dear husband. I forgot you weren't talking to Jane, but to a set of ears. I was his captive audience. "I think he was looking towards Superiorii Phorgiveness..." he answered. Apparently, the question was interesting enough for him to consider. "... what does it even matter?"

I didn't answer. Why would it even matter? He wasn't interested in what I had to say and I wasn't interested in being ignored. But I was agitated at the idea of my father mistreating Superiorii Phorgiveness. I needed to know what happened next.

"It doesn't. What happened next?" I asked.

"Superiorii Phorgiveness looked ashamed, but Superiorii Depherence! They could've murdered Joel in front of him and he would've had the same look on his face!" I didn't care! He was stuffing me with useless information! Just tell me what happened with Superiorii Phorgiveness, stupid cunt! "You might get to see his face tomorrow if Superiorii Faithfull has his way, though," he said.

"What do you mean?" I asked.

"I mean, Superiorii Faithfull wants to execute Joel Depherence for adultery and homosexuality."

"What...?" I exclaimed, sitting up in bed and giving James exactly what he wanted- undivided attention. His manner turned cooler and his actions were more calculated. He didn't look at me. Not even in my direction. He stood there, almost with his back toward me, reciting, begrudgingly, the events of the day. It was his way of saying, 'I'm worth every moment of your time, but you're not worth a second of mine.'

"Last night, Superiorii Phorgiveness walked down our hall to the room at the end," my heart sunk. He was talking too quickly through matters I wanted to hear gently. He was in our hall? He passed by my room? He went back to our room? Why? "He was checking rooms to make sure there were no impurities being committed, but it's the first time one of the four members officially inspected the rooms." So... he was just doing his job? "When he reached the last room, he found Joel having sex with the son of the man executed for homosexuality... The one executed a while before we were married... Do you know who I'm talking about?"

"Yes, I do," I answered a little too assertively, but James's tone was rising and the frustration towards Superiorii Phorgiveness's action was overwhelming me. Fortunately, James didn't notice. He didn't care if I answered him or not.

"Jonah!" he proudly declared, "Jonah! That was his name! Anyways, Superiorii Phorgiveness found Joel having sex with Jonah and when Joel noticed someone was watching him, he quickly tried defending himself, saying Jonah was his alternative, but that obviously doesn't matter. Joel doesn't have a healthy baby, so he doesn't get an alternative," I knew that, but he spoon-fed me this information as if I didn't. "According to Superiorii Phorgiveness, Jonah didn't say anything. He looked scared, but refused to talk... So Superiorii Faithfull said he was going to talk to the boy tonight and get the full story... to see if the boy was forced into sex or willingly participated," James turned around, but kept his stare glued to the floor until he reached the bed, flopped in, jumping me a millimeter from the bed as usual, and turned over to face away from me. "... but Superiorii Faithfull wants Joel executed. He made his feelings clear to everyone present... including Joel and his father. Neither he nor his father said anything," James laughed, "They were both too shocked."

"But..." I wondered aloud, forgetting who I was asking, "...is executing a successor allowed?"

"Your father argued it wasn't... He was the only one who said anything other than Superiorii Faithfull... but I think it was to spite Superiorii Faithfull."

"What's going to happen?" I asked, once again, forgetting who I was asking.

"I don't know," James answered curtly, brushing my silly question away from him as he adjusted himself further away from me and pulled the blankets towards him, "Mind your own business and let me sleep."

Chapter Thirteen

Attending the daily sermon taxed me that morning, but I ignored my mind's plight and focused on Juliet. Her father's big, deep, blue eyes were my envy. Blue eyes would've made my life better. Maybe it would've made Superiorii Phorgiveness love me? James treat me better? Maybe father would've treated me better? I compared myself to her.

My gaze turned heavy and fell to the floor. I could've been happy had I been born a different person. I looked at my mother's bare feet and pasted my eyes to her heels. I concentrated on breathing and swallowing. I didn't want to cry. I didn't want James to notice me. He liked his women equable, even when raping them, and if I didn't meet his standards, he would 'discipline' me until I learned my lesson. Why did he get to discipline me? Why couldn't I discipline him? The thought of me slapping him for a change... biting him, kicking him, scratching at his face, pushing him off the bed, screaming at him, tearing at his scalp... was enticing.

"*Stop crying!*" I would shout, "*Stop crying or I'll smack you harder!*" Give him a taste of his own medicine. Tell him I'm making him a better person, but he's just too ungrateful to appreciate my efforts.

I didn't know if it was bitterness or my right, maybe a mix of both, but I blamed them. I hated them. I looked up from my mother's heels, trailed my hot stare over her and father, and watched them exist in their indifference. I caught father flinch his stare from Superiorii Depherence towards his left a couple times, but my mother was staring blankly at Superiorii Depherence. She didn't care what he was saying. She was waiting for him to finish. It was a shared sentiment. No one in the congregation cared about Superiorii Depherence's lesson. They wanted the sermon to end to discuss how great it was among their little social circles, their cults within a cult. When I skimmed over Jeanette, I noticed the intense attention she, and women like her, was paying to Superiorii Depherence, but, unlike the rest, she needed to pay attention. How else was she supposed to enforce rules on others?

Men monopolized official power. Men who thirsted for control, power, and dominance could force their opinions over others if they were born into the right family. Women, on the other hand, were banned from exerting any official control, but when a woman thirsted for power, she controlled other women's lives on the social level. She controlled the congregation unofficially. Jeanette, her mother-in-law, and a couple random sisters were this type of woman. They were equally as rotten, cruel, vindictive, judgmental, aggressive, and capricious as the men in power.

I'm happy these power-hungry women were barred from power. I just wish those power-hungry men were barred, too.

Why did we even listen to them? The majority clearly didn't care, though they claimed otherwise, but it was more because they had to say they did. They couldn't give their opinions without considering the consequences. Maybe most people reach a point in their lives where they're convinced to remain complicit?

Was I complicit? I didn't want to age into these women who couldn't understand an inch of my misery, but for some reason, I felt my appearance shift into one indistinguishable from theirs. I was turning into my mother-in-law. James was already my father. And my child...? It was the first time I felt something for the poison growing inside me. I felt pity. I was bringing life into a world that only bred monsters. A cup of anxiety spilled from my heart into my stomach. Is it merciful to carve the child out before it tasted my misery? But then I realized... The ultimate control every individual has is over life and death. Women, in particular, are in a biological position where they can take dominion over this matter. I can create life. I can bring life into this world. But I can take it away.

I sat up in my seat, turned towards my right, and looked at James for a moment. He ignored me, but I'm sure he would've paid me much more attention if he was hearing my thoughts. He would've yanked me from my seat, thrown me to the ground, kicked my spine until it bruised and swelled, and bashed my teeth in, chanting for my death, begging for a new wife. But it wouldn't have mattered because I knew how to hurt him.

He told me he would smother our child if she was a girl. Not to save her from a loveless life of rape, but because he wanted a son worthy of his lineage. So, I decided if our child was a boy- I would smother it. Even if someone stopped me from smothering it, I would bounce it off the ground and hope it dies. If it didn't die, it would at least be lame and James would kill a lame child regardless of sex, so my revenge was inevitable. I would never bring another version of my father or James or Superiorii Faithfull or Joel or Superiorii Depherence into the world. I'd sooner kill myself to kill it within me than give life to such a monster.

I was sick of monsters. I was sick of people. I wanted to be alone in that little room at the end of the hall and live out the rest of my life there peacefully. I wanted to live my life autonomously, but it was impossible. How dare you control your own life? How dare you formulate your own opinions? Do you even love the Antifasi? Do you even love your parents? Do you love anyone besides yourself, you arrogant child? I don't know. Who cares...? Why do I have to be your focus? I'm not doing anything to you, so why are you obsessed with me? I was confused and frustrated and the questions kept scratching my brain and I could feel myself going mad. The only thing these people talked about was how much they loved the Antifasi and how they could feel him in their hearts, but I couldn't. I hated my father and felt cold towards my mother, but I had to love them. Why? The Antifasi never kept me company when I was alone or crying my eyes out in a corner. In fact, he was the root of all my problems. And my parents... My mother was hollow inside... And my father... How could I love someone who screamed at me and made me feel so inadequate? Even to this day, I still can't feel loved by anyone because of them and the congregation.

I can feel love. But I can't feel loved. And I think that's one of the greatest tortures in life. If not the greatest.

I'm sure my train of thought only lasted twenty minutes from its departure to its arrival, but once I returned to reality, I had spent years within my mind. I'm better equipped now to explain the concepts I was tripping over then, but when I first contemplated these matters, their weight was far heavier. They were foreign and complicated. To my knowledge, I was the only person considering any of these questions and I could very well have been right. But I didn't want to be alone in my thoughts. It only fueled my loneliness.

Thinking is an exhausting habit. I can't blame most people, including those within the congregation, for not wanting to indulge in it. I just don't understand how they couldn't to do it. I feel so naturally inclined to shred apart my realities, dreams, imaginations, the ills of society, and even my interests when I'm trying to sleep. They don't seem to even have opinions on rules which directly affect them. But how could they not formulate opinions of their own when it came to matters of the congregation? Were they so automated they defaulted to wherever the majority lied?

The sermon ended and an update was coming. Superiorii Faithfull stood up from his front row seat, walked his stubby legs over to the platform, his face more than composed, and his presence pushed Superiorii Depherence away from the stand. I don't know if the Superiorii coordinated updates before the sermons or if one member could approach the platform when the

177

sermon ended, but if they coordinated beforehand, why would Superiorii Depherence be so willing to step aside? This was the beginning of his son's execution.

"Superiorii Depherence," he said, barely acknowledging the man he was addressing, "I thank you for your dedication to this congregation... Your sermons are full of passion... You encourage obedience and submission to the Antifasi and to those the Antifasi has appointed, namely the Superiorii... And you manage to make a new sermon every day..."

Everyone was sitting up more stiffly in their seats, some shifting here and there, but not much. I looked over at my father and noticed a look of frozen expectation. He was unmoved. He was waiting. I looked over at Superiorii Phorgiveness and noticed the same look only with a tinge of concern in the corners of his lips and eyes where my father had aggression. Superiorii Depherence, standing on the platform behind Superiorii Faithfull, was watching Superiorii Faithfull with his head somewhat bowed. He was looking at him with softer expectation, but the weak man had no presence. He just wanted to keep out of Superiorii Faithfull's way. The congregation, on the other hand, were all listening intently, including myself. Why was Superiorii Faithfull praising Superiorii Depherence this way? This wasn't an update. Updates never started like this. They were a practical matter and often done promptly and coldly. This was more expressive. Superiorii Faithfull was threatening him.

"It's rare to find a man who wants to live up to the Antifasi's standards, guiding a congregation filled with people poisoned with the tendency to live impurely. It's the same poison the Superiorii are tainted with, but we, among the congregation, should be the furthest from impurity. Otherwise, how can we protect and guide our congregation in accordance to the Antifasi's laws?" Superiorii Faithfull didn't acknowledge anyone, but I noticed his eyes linger over one spot from time to time. When he asked the question, his eyes paused even longer over that spot, so, in my curiosity, I looked down his gaze's direction.

It led to the same boy who had sat next to his mother, shaking during his father's execution like he was shaking now.

Superiorii Faithfull was only acknowledging Jonah. And Jonah was looking up to Superiorii Faithfull- horrified.

Superiorii Faithfull was going to announce Joel's rape and condemn his actions. He was going to set protections for children and push forth his reforms. It was a prediction easy enough to make based on observation and intuition, but that wasn't what caught my attention. It was a minor detail I almost overlooked, but it was a detail which grew until I made it meaningful. Jonah was shaking. He was shaking the same way I did. I looked back at him, trying to skim a glimpse like I had during his father's 'trial', and noticed him shaking even harder. Had he noticed me? If he had, was he thinking about me? Would he realize I understood his shaking? I wanted him to hear my thoughts, '*I understand you... but do you understand me? Do you want to understand me? You're not alone... I'm here... We can be together away from everyone...*' I kept looking at him until he flinched his stare from Superiorii Faithfull to me.

I didn't want to be noticed. I was a ghost, not an actual person, so when he acknowledged me, it unnerved me. I flipped myself back around, but the motion was so sudden both Jeanette and James looked and soon enough judged me.

"What is wrong with you, Jane?" Jeanette complained first.

"Nothing," I tried, but answering someone who hissed in your ear is a mind-splitting practice.

"*Jane!*" James called, trying to yank my attention, "*Sit still, look forward, and pay attention. Stop making such a pain of yourself all the time- it's annoying.*"

"Okay," I reflexively answered, wanting the whole affair to be over. I even nodded. I accepted his criticism without thought. The only thing I considered worth thinking about was whether or not Jonah had watched their reaction. I didn't want to look back again because either way I was going to further humiliate myself, but my curiosity got the better of me and I turned. He had seen everything. He was considerate enough to look away, pretending he hadn't, but my heart dropped into a pool of insecurities and cleansed me of any trace of pride. However, my mind was adamant on cleaning up the mess I made.

Sweep your glance over the congregation. Crane your neck a little to make it seem as if you're looking at someone far away. Someone that isn't Jonah. Make sure it's obvious enough for him to notice even from the corner of his eye. Slowly turn yourself all the way back and look forward; don't even think about looking away from Superiorii Faithfull. My mind was quite meticulous when it came to detail. It couldn't help considering every little thing that might go wrong and preemptively taking care of it. Not even this elaborate 'rouse' was enough for it. A grander gesture of indifference was needed, but the fact I couldn't think of one, saved me from even further humiliation.

"... would the Antifasi think if one of the members of the Superiorii was actually corrupting his chosen congregation rather than guiding it according to his written laws in the Den Amfisvito?" I regretted my distraction. This 'update' had never happened before- and who knew if it was going to happen again? Who, other than Superiorii Faithfull and maybe Jonah, knew where this 'update' was leading? How was I supposed to catch up? "He has appointed us as the members of the congregation best suited to resist impurity, but impurity, nonetheless, has caught up to us and we must cleanse ourselves of its filth." I jumped to an impossible conclusion when he said this, but it was too nonsensical, wild even, to seriously consider. "There is one among us whose appointed successor has corrupted our congregation and dragged one of our very own children down a path of impurity..."

I thought he was talking about me.

The congregation was breathless. There was not a single dull or sleepy eye, but widened stares. My father was leaning in his seat, pointing the bullet of his direction towards Superiorii Faithfull. I looked over at Superiorii Phorgiveness again. He wasn't breathing. His chest wasn't moving. He was sitting there-completely frozen. It killed me to see it, but... Superiorii Phorgiveness was grabbing his wife's hand... I never knew he considered her someone in his life. I thought she was nothing more than an imposition to him. She wasn't even holding him back. It was more like he was grabbing the arm of a chair for physical support rather than the hand of his wife for emotional support, but his grabbing her still killed me inside. I would've held him back. But he didn't want me. No one did.

"... is saving him from facing the same trial any other member would face if found committing the same crime. Is that something that honors the Antifasi's name, though? Having your father be a current member of the Superiorii does not mean you can live a life committing impurity. The very purpose of the Superiorii is to keep the congregation from committing them." I noticed Jeanette nodding and realized that she, her mother-in-law, and a few other women of the congregation, both the relatively reasonable and the irrational, were agreeing with Superiorii Faithfull's sentiment. The men, in general, looked incensed. Nothing too notable, but their faces had hardened. They were offended at being denied power in preference for someone who had been given it since birth and had abused it- even though they all would've abused it anyway. And others were probably angry over the idea of being misguided. Either way, everyone was paying attention to Superiorii Faithfull... except me... I was too busy noticing what everyone else was doing.

"Joel Depherence..."

I inhaled sharply, my eyes widened, my lips parted, and I couldn't breathe. I was frozen in expectation, but everyone else was gasping, shifting, murmuring, and staring at Joel's crimson face. His manner was trembling. His eyes were darting back and forth- just like his father's. "… was found committing an impurity with a little boy…" I couldn't breathe. Even when 'trials' happened, the soon-to-be executed were never called by their names. They were monsters or puppets of the Fos Terata, but never individuals. "… Joel threatened him into silence…" Superiorii Faithfull informed. We were never told the charges leveled against the damned. I was sharply blasted from my mind into the present. "…If the boy had spoken out, Joel would've had him thrown into the left furnace …" Everyone gasped and the rhythm of rage was pulsing through their breaths, "He would've used the Antifasi against a child." The murmurs grew louder. "He would've burned a boy alive for the sake of his lust." The anger boiling over the congregation was now burning Joel Depherence alive. I didn't look at Joel to satisfy my curiosity. I was too enraptured in Superiorii Faithfull's presence.

There was something honest about him… Something endearing… powerful… and, in that moment, I confess… "How far away have we fallen from the Antifasi's righteous path to create a world where impurities like these are allowed? Children being abused and used for the most disgusting of appetites only men could design… Joel and others like him are just as disgusting as the acts they've committed… I want to cleanse the congregation of their filth…" I admired Superiorii Faithfull. I looked over at Jeanette and noticed the warmth she had for him in her eyes. She looked like she was in love with him. She was dressing him with the same gaze I clothed Superiorii Phorgiveness in countless times. But I understood her now… I understood Superiorii Faithfull's appeal… and I was supporting it. Despite Jeanette's mania, Superiorii Faithfull wasn't psychotic. He was a passionate man supporting something noble. The abolishment of systematic child abuse.

I just find it odd how quickly my simple mind forgot about his advocacy for genital mutilation and methods of inquisition.

Chapter Fourteen

That night, like all since my pregnancy, I rested on my side, away from James, facing the stone wall, wide awake. I wasn't thinking of a happy future. I only now felt slightly guilty for the abstract thoughts spiraling from my questions. If I hadn't been so numb, I'm sure I would've felt the pangs of guilt, but this wasn't a concern anymore. The painful truth was I was trapped. And I was trying to free my mind from my body. Everything that touched me, the blankets, the mattress, my clothes, were clasping me to this life. There were phantom chains locked around my ankles long enough to give me the illusion of freedom, but I was still a prisoner. If I kicked my feet out, I could feel the metal anklets tug at James's ankles, the bed, and the wall. I would first have to free myself from our bed and then James before I could reach the wall, but even if I managed to unfasten myself from these three captors- what if I was tied to yet another possessor? What if the chain was tied to my parents' room? To the main hall? Where would I even be free to go if I unchained myself completely?

I was trapped. I couldn't go anywhere. This was my world. I would spend the rest of my life as James's wife. I would birth and die in this empty, stone room. The congregation was my coffin. And I was born nailed into it.

There was a knot of vinegar twisting itself above my right lung, percussing my heart. Stones were dropped in a pond of all my unsorted emotions and little ripples were marching away towards neighboring territories. My underarms felt heavier, my stomach emptier, my esophagus shakier, beating out a rhythm unnatural to the human system, and my throat jammed. There was a blockage at the base of my throat which rose and rose and rose until it was a bullet lodged between my ribs, but the pain was ambitious. I was struggling to keep my lips together, but my eyes watered. I was going to be overtaken soon. Its pace grew more diligent, churning itself harder and harder, spiraling itself up the tunnel of my throat, and once it reached my tongue, I choked out a sob.

Tears were downpouring. My lower eyelids already hot and heavy. They'd be swollen the next morning and I'd have to powder on even more ash from the furnace to hide the discoloration, but closing my eyes hurt. There was too much baggage behind them to keep them shut comfortably. I had to keep looking up to keep them from exploding within my skull, but I kept biting my lip until the ridges of my dirty teeth were marked upon my chin. I couldn't make a sound. If I shook just a little too hard, I risked waking James up. I had already suffered those consequences.

Last I woke him up, I felt guilty for having cried and appreciated James for withholding his hand. He only screamed at me for my audacity. He studied all day and well into the night to prepare himself for the role of Superiorii and here his spoiled wife was crying beside him when she had everything in the world to make her happy. I was sleeping in a bed now, wasn't I? He didn't touch me anymore now, didn't he? So, why was I so unhappy? I was even holding the Antifasi's gift inside of me! I should've felt happier than ever and praised my husband like all the other pregnant women before me. Despite the abuse warping my common sense, I still managed to come up with a concrete reason as to why it seemed all other pregnant women besides myself praised their husbands. It wasn't because they felt indebted. It was because the louder women exuded so much pride it overshadowed the other women who were silent on their pain. I felt guilty for thinking this, but the guilt was no longer pooling. It was dripping into a deeper well of hatred, anger, numbness, sadism, and an addictive sort of bitterness that brought me a sense of peace. You see, the bitterness corroded my insecurity. I was becoming more powerful through my growing hatred.

Every time I felt pain, every time I berated myself over James's gaslighting games, especially the oxymoronically sharp, dull sentiment of woe, I defaulted into this well and washed myself with the waters of hatred. Though my eyes were watering, and I still needed to bite my lip that night, my imagination was soothing me into a more controlled state.

'Think about it, Jane. Just think about it,' my mind whispered, 'You turn over... Sit up... Take your pillow within your hands... tightly gripping each side... and climb out of the blankets... slowly... quietly... Can you imagine what he'd do to you if you woke him up...? Can you imagine it... Think about it, Jane... Just think about it,' my heart pulled upwards to run from the poison, but I'd force myself to guzzle it down. It made me stronger. It made me more powerful. 'You would climb over him... pressing your knees on either side of him like he did to you... and you would take that pillow... and you would put it over his face... gently... No sense in rushing things... No sense in waking him up... He'll soon enough realize he's not breathing and that's when you pull the pillow down and keep it there for only moments... The more he struggles, the quicker it happens... and soon enough... You can go to bed... move all you want...' I felt the idea tantalize my taste buds and my mouth watered, 'Think about it, Jane. Just think about it,' and I was, of course. The idea was so simple. It was so within my reach. I could do it and maybe, just maybe, one night I would.

But, why not this one?

If I put the task off, then would I do it tomorrow night? The night after that one? If not, then exactly when did I plan on unravelling the chain? I lacked courage. I was living within a cage too small for my frame, my bones pressed into new contortions, my muscles eating themselves to free up space, but I had grown accustomed to the ardor. Change might've bettered my life, but it was change I had to get used to. If I wanted to smother

James in his sleep, then I would need to get up, pick up the pillow, climb over him, and eventually press down with all my might. That required effort. The task was too exhausting and troublesome. I would just fail anyways, so what was the point? However, once James rolled over, going through two whole revolutions, pulling away the little blanket I had left to cover my arm, the answer became clear. When exposure licked my upper arm, hatred sunk its teeth in and embittered my mind. I now had the clarity, purpose, and courage I needed to do away with this parasite.

I rolled onto my back and stared up at the ceiling, incredibly conscious of the pillow crushed beneath my head. James was going to die. My victim was sleeping beside me, still alive. I wondered what the transition between life and death would look like. I contented myself in the knowledge that I would soon learn. I pressed my forearms onto the mattress and dragged my bottom up, pulling my legs along with it like cans on a string. I looked over at James, hoping I hadn't woken him up yet, and noticed him still sleeping. Still vulnerable. But, on his side. He was facing away from me. I peeped over his shoulder to see the angle of his nose and mouth, but the harder I looked, the more I realized how challenging it would be to suffocate him. He wasn't resting upwards like I had imagined him. My idea already wasn't going according to plan and this change was something I most certainly wasn't comfortable with. It gave me more reason to believe I would fail, so I gave up.

I sat there, sinking in my failure. No matter what I set my mind to, I would never accomplish it even if I did my best. Happiness would always elude me because I was Jane and being Jane meant I was doomed to unhappiness.

Staring at the wall, I followed the lines from where the bricks were cemented together until I circled around and landed right back where I started. When that happened, I looked at the whole slab of wall. The path my eyes were following had vanished into its new identity. It was a wall now. Just a wall. My eyes focused and unfocused at the patch of stones until my peripheral vision kicked in and recognized the entirety of the wall. I was sitting in a room. It had four walls and a stone ceiling. I was surrounded, but there was a door. It was opposite the wall I had been staring at. You could use it to leave. My critical mind throughout this entire awareness process was dormant and floating somewhere else. The only question looping through my empty skull, echoing its inquiry until it meant nothing, was, 'What should I do now?' It was the prompt question that focused and unfocused my eyes throughout the stare. If I thought of an answer, more of the wall was acknowledged.

'You could try going back to sleep again or at least lie down...' it suggested, but the idea wasn't satisfactory. I didn't want to return to the monotony after having almost completely changed my life. It would've served as a sore reminder of how foolish I am. So, the cement lines disappeared and more of the wall was seen.

'You could sit up for the rest of the night and wait for morning...' it suggested and, though the idea seemed like a natural thing to do, I knew my back wouldn't allow it. I've tried sitting during my sleepless nights and after a while, my back burned in certain places- especially around my shoulder blades and mid to lower back. The slab of wall disappeared within its surroundings and the entire wall was visible now.

'You could visit the room...' it suggested. 'The room' being the room I used to spend my nights with Superiorii Phorgiveness in. I hadn't considered visiting it since the accident and even looking down the end of the hallway was abrading to me. I had been thoroughly humiliated. Every time I thought about the room, a little priest rang a church bell at the bottom of my chest, reminding me of how utterly shocking my accident was. I had bled on Superiorii Phorgiveness. I ran from him like a child, leaving him to wake up alone and bloodied.

It was the only place I knew I'd be safe escaping into,

though. I couldn't wander the halls without risking getting caught by some dutiful Superiorii that decided to study a little longer that night. I couldn't look into any room and hope it was empty. Despite the congregation being small, and my having lived there for the first half of my life, I still didn't know who lived in which room. It was something I felt self-conscious about because apparently everyone else did, so it was another reason for me to feel stupid. I knew the room at the end of my hallway was empty, though. It was the only safe room I was aware of. I wanted to leave. I felt nostalgic that night. As my bitterness kept spilling into untouched parts of my consciousness, I found myself contrasting this new Jane against the old Jane.

The old Jane was an insecure, anxious mess who bent beneath pressure easier than a twig cracking between two hands, but looking back, I romanticized my past, as most do when miserable or forgetful, and focused on the happier moments. The sparkles I felt when I was with Superiorii Phorgiveness. The little glints of genuine happiness I felt at the prospect of marrying him. The unbroken, unstained, intact dreams I clung onto as reality. I was a monster now. I hated what I had become, even though I hated myself before for a different set of reasons, and wished so much to return to the old ways, but I lost the map. I couldn't go back. I was lost within this world of trial and error after error after error. I wanted to know what was the right way of being. What I should and shouldn't do, how I should and shouldn't behave, what I should and shouldn't think, but it was a mystery to me. Everyone seemed to know all the answers. My persona was nothing more than an amalgamation of flaws and I was failure incarnate. Thus, I wanted to become another person, even if I was the same person from a different time. Going to the room was the only way I could physically bring myself to that world and I felt, in my tarred heart, that it was the first step to changing my life wholly.

I skirted my legs through the blankets over the side of the bed. I slowly descended my feet through the sliver of space between the bed and wall barely big enough to fit the width of one foot. When my ankle clanked against the wall, though, and that numbing, rippling, tickling, and disabling pain riveted up to my knee, I realized the grace I would need to continue. I wrapped my palm around the stinging bone and choked it to centralize the pain. Once it faded down to a more tolerable level, I lowered it back to where it was supposed to be, carefully, and sat there plotting my next move. I would have to stand up, but how? I had to have one foot over the other to fit through the sliver of space, but it was an unnatural position. I wouldn't have my balance, so I strongly risked falling against the bed, not necessarily hard, but hard enough, and waking James. What if I kept my hands on the bed, though? It would require some level of skill in the art of contortion, but I was still a child, so I could muster up a natural talent. Not to mention, it eliminated the possibility of me falling over because I would have 'support beams' sustaining me. I would then clamber over, raising one foot over the other, doing my best to keep them away from the stone wall, until I reached the end of the bed where I would be free to silently eek away into my past. The only problem I didn't recognize, though, was the practical application of the process. Sure, it all sounded fine and well in my head, but I didn't include variables into my calculations. What if I was off? What if the bed wasn't lined up parallel against my wall, but on an intersecting angle? What if I clanked my ankles against the wall again and slumped back onto the bed to relieve them of pressure? What if I stepped on something sharp? What if I accidentally kicked the bed a little too hard?

These were all mistakes I made while playing out my 'well thought out plan'. Surprisingly, James didn't wake up, though. Before then, I had never noticed how heavy a sleeper he was. When I slumped onto the bed, the motion was enough to wake a normal person up. It was hard enough and I made the bed creak, but he was unaffected. Apparently, only my whimpering was loud enough to irk him out of sleep. Had I known how profoundly he slept, I probably would've gone through with murdering him, but the moment had come and gone. I was now at the foot of 'our' bed, tip-toeing my way through the darkness. The romantic memory of childhood flushed my stomach of its vinegar and filled it up with the dripping honey of sweeter times as I made my way to the door. Once I reached it, the idea of it creaking didn't frighten me as much as it would've had James been a lighter sleeper. I just slowly opened it, doing my best to quickly, but softly go through the two long creaks it made as best as I could, and then walked out, closing it behind me with a soft boom.

Looking down the longer than I remember hallway, I felt the same pangs of regret I'd felt before. The humiliation, the ache of menstruation forcing me to collapse before my parents' bedroom door, I even missed sleeping on the floor. I missed my parents. They were strangers now. I didn't know what happened at night between them anymore. I could only make accurate assumptions based off my experience, but I wanted to know exactly what had happened since I'd left. That was my world. I had been uninvited. I was an adult now. I had my own world of responsibilities and expectations to attend to. I took a step, thoughtlessly, towards the door at the end of the hallway, forcing myself to make the journey in body, though I was helpless in mind. I was still focused on the unexpected angle of the bed. But I trailed down the hallway, physically feeling the memories bounce off my chest and brush past my arms like fingertips skating by, absent-mindedly.

Nothing was real. The floor I was walking on was a floor, but what was beneath that floor? What was outside these walls? These questions were particularly forbidden to wonder about within the congregation. The Superiorii demanded we reject these thoughts in specific because it could lead us into the worst temptation of all- breaking the boards on a window and stepping into the light. The boards were secured over the main hall and there were only a few rooms with windows in them, my room with Superiorii Phorgiveness was one of them, but that's why it was empty. Any room with a window in it was kept empty to keep members of the congregation from privately escaping into the land of the Fos Terata, or the outside world, they were one in the same, and bringing back their soiled corpses to poison the rest of the congregation. However, throughout my childhood, I couldn't help myself from questioning these things. It wasn't until my dad 'taught me the lesson' of repression, though I was a bad student, that I learned how to quiet these questions until they were nothing more than a whisper in the wind. Background music to the more prevalent questions in my head. The new ones I wouldn't dare ask my father, or anyone, but Superiorii Phorgiveness, for that matter. What was above the ceiling? Where are we? Is this a world within a world? If yes, then is that world outside our world within another world, too? How many worlds are there? Is it an infinite number of worlds within worlds within worlds or are there different, unrelated worlds that exist alone and empty? What were those worlds like? Did the Antifasi rule them all or just this one? If he doesn't rule them, then who does? Do they have their own Antifasi? What if it's a woman, though? I want a woman Antifasi! I wonder what his or her rules are? I bet they're nicer than the Antifasi.

Snap.

That's when my mind jumped from the angle of the bed preoccupation to the 'you just blasphemed' fear. My old anxiety took a giant inhale within me and revived itself for a moment, like gas passing through a cadaver, but when I thought about James and my parents and all the anguish I was forced to endure in the Antifasi's name, I smothered the anxiety before it could conquer me again. Bitterness washed over me, drowning and washing out the tinge of my former self, and I was numb again. Cynical. I no longer felt excitement or anxiety from returning to that room anymore. It was just a room to me now. I was still walking towards it, but the journey didn't feel like a 'journey' anymore. I was just walking down the hall. The door before me was just a door. It didn't matter that every time I had grasped its handle before, I felt a jump of adrenaline because my beloved Superiorii Phorgiveness was waiting for me on the other side. I might've felt the feeling for a split second, a result of Pavlovian conditioning no doubt, but no one was waiting for me. I knew it. That knowledge stabbed my hope in front of the consulate of my hatred which stood by in approval and then fled into the numbness of my night. I clicked the handle open and pushed the door ahead, letting it creak out its blistering moans. If someone heard, I wouldn't have cared. Nothing mattered anymore.

I just wanted to be alone...

... but apparently, that was too much to ask.

When the door came to a soft stop, just a few inches away from hitting the wall, I noticed a figure in the darkness. It was huddled up against the left corner, much like Superiorii Phorgiveness was the last time we were together. My eyes lit up, my shoulders felt as light as a feather, and I lost my breath. I could feel my heart standing on its tippy toes, trying to peak over my chest to see for itself whether I was laying eyes on my beloved one more time in our own secret world, but soon enough it fumbled over and fell. The figure was too small to be him. My eyes deceived me into seeing what I wanted to see. I was just looking at a cowering, little boy, sitting in silent expectation.

'Leave,' my mind demanded, but my legs rebelled and trudged forward. 'Go back,' my arms forwent the order and closed the door behind me. 'Stop!' it pled, but my vocal cords readied themselves to be used.

"*Jonah?*" I whispered.

No response. He was just staring at me, most likely scared of what I might do next, but soon enough I saw him nod. "*Yes...?*"

C hapter Fifteen

I didn't know what to say in return. I couldn't get away with a pause and exit. He was expecting me to finish a thought within the stony confines of this abandoned room. My abandoned room. My home with Superiorii Phorgiveness. Jonah was a drifter taking refuge within my former home. It felt invasive, but there was nothing I could do. The sanctity, and personal sanctuary, of this space was in the past now. I missed my childhood. It was stolen from me only three months ago, yet this room already had foreign energy to me.

"Why are you here?" I finally asked. It was the simplest, most obvious question I could've asked, but it was the only question I could conjure up. In fact, just thinking of that 'simple' question was an arduous task because rambling thoughts were skiing through my head, muttering their inappropriate thoughts at the root of my scalp.

"I don't know..." was his innocent reply. I could tell from his tone he thought he'd be in trouble for being somewhere he didn't belong, but I detected a hint of surprise as well. Jonah never wanted to do anything wrong, but somehow everything he did, even just lounging about in solitude within an empty room for a night, was naughty. I wondered how his parents disciplined him...

His mother seemed too meek a character to employ harsh, corporal punishment. It was more probable that she relied on pinching and shoving rather than beating. However, I can clearly imagine a formidable woman like her naturally privy to emotional and psychological abuse. Jonah was probably never a good enough son for her. She probably nipped at him day to day for it. I can't, and couldn't, quite remember his father, though. The only memory I have of him was the day of his execution, but that isn't an accurate standard to measure a man by. Men were more likely to use harsh, corporal punishment, though. I couldn't imagine one of them sparing the rod even if it didn't mean spoiling the child. There was an undercurrent of pent up frustration in both parents, from unfulfilled passions or repression in general, that, from their point of view, could only be expressed against their child.

They relieve their own madness in breaking their children to feel the power they didn't have when their parents and the congregation were breaking them.

This spew of realizations didn't come to me at that moment, of course. My hopelessly platonic/romantic heart was searching for consolation in the soul of someone else. Jonah seemed lost, thus not domineering as is typical of his sex. He seemed more vulnerable than defensive. His countenance was soft and I noted his tenderness which was typically a hidden or totally absent quality in most. He seemed... approachable... I wanted to be friends with him... I wanted to tell him all my problems and have him hold me. Despite the lethal stigma of members from opposite sexes being alone together, I didn't consider our circumstance to fall beneath that law. I thought my marriage and his boyhood, though he was only a little younger than myself, maybe even older, in fact, he could've been the same age, exempted us. It wasn't like it was my mother and Superiorii Phorgiveness who were alone in that room together. Jonah and I were just children. All I wanted was for someone to understand me and talk to me without any reservations and I assumed, in my solipsistic, childish mind, that all he wanted was the same.

"Did you want to be alone?" I asked, tripping over the last word. It's odd how one could think so much, they forget how to speak. I was saying something sincerer than the typical, 'Yes, I did like the sermon (that I paid no attention to),' which activated my anxiety and flustered my speech.

"I don't know..." he answered again after a pause. His tone cried out a little, but he was more frustrated with himself than with me. He kept looking in my direction because he was interested in my presence, I could tell, but I couldn't read into it at the time. I just felt he didn't want me to leave. I wasn't annoying him...

I wasn't being ignored. I was wanted. My being fully acknowledged pierced my heart with this radiating, peaceful excitement that I knew was too fleeting to become addictive. However, I still relished how I was being treated. He wasn't judging me. He seemed open to me. I needed to seize the moment and take as much advantage of it as I could because I knew, in minutes, he was going to realize how unworthy I was of his company. I could feel a pulse in my palms beat at intervals of one second and my chest flush with anxiety. My mind either crawled into a corner of my body or escaped me because I no longer felt it governing me. I was living by the unintelligible words passing through my teeth, "Would you mind if I stayed here with you, then?" I finally gutted out of myself.

"No," his head shook, but I didn't quite understand what he meant. He seemed kind, but he said no... and my presence always inconvenienced others, so it was only natural for me to conclude he meant he wanted me to leave. So, I took a step back, not wanting to clarify matters because I didn't want to be aggressive, and said, "Oh... okay."

"Why are you here?" he asked, so sweetly I felt the otherworldly experience again. I even forgot I was on my way out.

"I just wanted to be alone," I answered.

"Me, too."

"I thought you said you didn't know why you were here," I ignorantly remarked, not recognizing how sometimes it's difficult to conceptualize a reason into words when it's only ever loomed within your mind in the language intelligible only to oneself.

"I didn't, but you reminded me," he answered, smiling...

Why was he smiling at me? Did he like me? Was he just being nice? Maybe he knew I wanted a friend and was offering himself up as a volunteer. It did always feel like people could read my mind, so what made him any different? "Can I..." I swallowed, trying not to give away how nervous I was even though I could feel my face burn, "... can I sit there?" I asked, pointing at the spot next to him.

"Yes," he answered, rushing away from his spot to make some room for me, even sweeping the dust from the floor beside him, despite the room being empty. Though his attention was an antibiotic for the infection rotting my mind- I found myself judging him nonetheless. I don't know why and I didn't think beyond it at the time, but I couldn't help thinking less of him for his kindness towards me. He had to be pathetic to be so attentive towards me otherwise he would've ignored me like the others had, but why were his standards so low? Was it because he was my inferior? Was he even worth my time? Should I have asked him to leave from the beginning... considering his nervous nature, I'm sure he would've complied immediately.

I walked towards the spot next to him, though not too close to him, begrudgingly, as if I was taking my seat next to a creepy relative. When I sat down, with a sizable distance between the two of us, Jonah didn't scoot closer, he respected my space, and didn't look over at me either. He had his knees pressed up against his chest, his arms holding his knees in place, and was staring down at his feet. He was clearly thinking about something.

"Why did you want to be alone?" I asked.

I couldn't stand the silence. I felt I owed him conversation now. I also, to a lesser degree, still wanted to see how alike we were. I no longer wanted him to understand me and I didn't care if he liked me, but I wanted to make him feel indebted towards me. If he was my inferior, I wanted to make sure he knew he had a benevolent master. By getting to know his underlying feelings, I could help him feel less alone and he would adore me.

He swallowed and bit his lip with his one front tooth. His eyes darted three times- from a corner of a stone before me, to the other corner, to a third corner, and then his brows knitted. "I don't know..." he finally shrugged, bowing his head towards his knees while drowning his gaze down towards the space between his laps and stomach. That chasm seemed quite intimate for some reason. I felt an urge to lower his right arm, blocking me from the space, and lay my head within it, enveloping myself in his warmth. Not only would it be a comfort towards me, a tender touch, something daring, and a mark of my rebellion against James and everyone who forced me into marrying him, but it would push Jonah to reveal his true persona. I wanted him to open up. I wanted him to tell me who he was. I wanted to get inside his head and see how alike we were- just to see if I wasn't the only one who thought the way I thought.

"Do you feel alone?" I asked.

"I usually am..." he confessed.

The distinction between being alone and feeling alone had been a blur to me as a 'child', or before I was married off, but once I was with James, I perfectly understood the difference between the states. Being alone was something I usually preferred except when I could be with someone who was worth sacrificing my comfort for- like Superiorii Phorgiveness. Feeling alone was a permanent, haunting fixture within my soul which hollowed me without remedy. As a child, Superiorii Phorgiveness cured my loneliness. As a married 'woman'... child... solitude cured my loneliness.

"So am I," I said, doing my best to prod the concept I barely understood myself, "but do you feel sad about... being alone?"

"Um... I don't know..." he answered which dropped my heart sharply into my stomach, "... what do you mean...?" and with that, my heart snapped right back up. He still cared enough to listen to me. But, what did that say about him? There was something wrong with him.

"I mean," I drew a sharp inhale, giving away my tension at having to explain something I barely grasped myself, but I blamed him for my discomfort. If he wasn't so daft, I wouldn't have to ramble like an idiot, "do you ever feel... sad... about... being alone?" I repeated myself, throwing in an extra word for emphasis this time. How couldn't this fool understand what I meant? It was so clear. I shrugged to indicate to him the end of my explanation, but when I noticed his round eyes enlarge, I continued talking, "Does being around people make you feel sad?" I could feel my words slamming against him now.

"I-..." he stammered. I was making him nervous, but I brushed his anxiety off and blamed him for his own feelings. I was asking him simple questions I wanted answers to and he was refusing me my sought-after replies, "I... don't... know..." He lingered a few moments longer to utter the final word, expecting me to cut him off before he licked it out of his mouth, but I waited, feeling heat bubble up against my neck, until he finished.

I stared at him, trying my best to seem approachable and benevolent the way I wanted to seem, and I honestly thought, in my ignorance, I was succeeding. However, the flames chipping up from my chest were whipping away in my eyes and their hellish heat was burning Jonah through my gaze. My tight smile was forced and on the brink of a scowl. I thought my smile was just as pleasant as any of my other smiles- which was true. Little did I know, none of my smiles were pleasant. Especially not this one, "How do you not know?" I finally asked, trying to keep the corners of my lips curled upwards.

And Jonah, in response, uttered the dreadful, "I don't know," once again.

'How do you not know!' I wanted to scream. The offense, though not intended on his part, though I didn't care whether it was intentional or unintentional, was far too strong for me to cope with. The mask I was hiding behind was cracking and revealing the slivers of frustration I had bubbling beneath my skin. He didn't care about me. He didn't care enough to talk about his problems, so we could relate to each other and take solace in one another. He didn't even think about his problems. He was another thoughtless loafer coasting through the congregation ignorantly with no capacity for critical thought or deep emotion. He was another waste of space. I was, again, the odd one who thought far beyond the parameters of what should've been focused on. The one with no clear perception of reality. The one who wasted her time living inside her head. The one who sacrificed being normal, superficially happy, and pleasant for a further understanding of nuances in her reality. All the details everyone missed. All things people shrugged off, I studied.

"Oh," I answered.

I gave him a few quick nods, my chin pointing slightly higher than normal. I understood what he meant by 'I don't know'. He wanted me to leave him alone. He was subtly pushing me away and I was more than happy to oblige. It clarified his character for me. He didn't have the audacity necessary to tell me to leave him alone from the beginning, so instead he dragged my hopeful self through the embarrassment of unrequited confessions. He had stolen my feelings and knew me better than I knew him. I disdained the thief.

I pointed my feet away from him and folded my arms over my living belly. Why wouldn't it kick like the other women said it would?

"Do you ever feel sad about being alone?"

My heart sprinted like a gymnast, jumped, sprung into the air, grabbed the high bar, flipped, once, twice, three times, dismounted, and stuck the landing. I was excited again. Jonah did want to understand me. I was wrong. He wasn't trying to push me away. He was confused about what he was feeling because maybe... he never talked about it with anyone before, too.

He didn't know how to verbalize his deeper thoughts. And I was jumping to conclusions based on my unstable perception of the situation rather than keeping an open mind and an objective viewpoint, so I didn't associate our encounter with my experiences with others from the past. It's a shame I didn't realize that then.

I jumped to yet another conclusion. Since I was excited, the conclusion was an ideal rather than the worst.

He was in love with me... He was fascinated with me the way I was with him. Maybe he was my superior after all?

The idea of us being on equal planes was unfathomable to me. I had only ever observed and had relationships where one partner was lesser than the other. Yes. I did crave a mutual connection with someone where we understood each other and felt like each other's home. Someone who would let me sit before the fireplace of their heart and warm me up from the cold world outside. The idea was just something I made up, though. An impossibility within my imagination filled with kisses and genuine laughter. Even when I was with Superiorii Phorgiveness, the closest definition of tenderness I had, I saw him as my superior. There was no mutual connection. No confessions between two lost souls being found. So, with Jonah, my mind was still working within this pattern.

"I do..." I confessed, feeling my chest drop in and pump out harder and harder, "... do you?" I asked, forgetting I had already asked him this before.

"Yes," he answered.

"I thought you said you didn't know?" I questioned, sliding my toes back towards him.

"I didn't, but..." he thought, breathing heavier, too, "... I didn't know if it was okay to tell you..."

"Why do you think it's okay to tell me now?" I was expressing myself more aggressively than I intended to, but I couldn't soften my tone without being artificially pleasant which to me was far worse. I would later realize my tone wasn't that aggressive, though. I thought it was because James conditioned me into thinking anything above a meek tone was raising my voice.

"Because you told me how you felt..."

His eyes were brown like James's, but where James's eyes were empty abysses, Jonah's were cozy and lulling. He looked at me with the fondness of an old soul looking at a tree he watched grow from a sapling. It was inviting, waiting, and accepting. There was no judgment, no malice, no defense. There was no cowardice, no submission, and no weakness. Just the tender blaze of a controlled fire crackling within his chest, willing to warm anyone who came near. And I felt warm. When he answered me, the words 'you', 'how', and 'felt' stuck out to me like ridges on a block of firewood and I was feeling my palms over them. I could hardly breathe for how ethereal the moment was. My heart was in a world with a different atmosphere now, but my body was still back in the congregation. I was a spirit walking through this moment and there was no sheen I could hide behind to mask my true feelings. I feared I wouldn't survive the change.

I wanted to say something to him, but it would've corrupted the moment. Words are tools we use to recreate times, but not to feel them. Instead, we felt each other's pains together in silence. 'My father's not a kind man. He was violent towards my mother and I. And my mother's a shell of a woman. She was robbed of her life and allowed others to rob me of mine. My husband is evil through and through. He has no regard for the feelings of others except if they feel he's too weak for the role of Superiorii. He raped me until I was pregnant... All I ever think about is killing him... and this thing inside of me... And the only person who showed me kindness is a stranger to me now. Do you understand?' Jonah nodded.

'My father was a quiet man who kept to himself only to be

executed before a congregation of people who approved of his death. I was expected to watch him burn without a shred of emotion. Joel used my father's execution as blackmail against me soon after. He raped me for nights because I was scared he'd tell the Superiorii I was impure just like my father and they'd burn me, too. My mother is a cold woman who's never shown me love and is more like a stone than a mother. And I've never had anyone show me kindness. Do you understand?' I shook my head. I couldn't fathom the pain of knowing your father was burned alive let alone in front of you.

It's funny how much can be said just in a stare.

"Jonah...?" I called.

"Yes, Jane?" he answered... He knew my name. This whole time he wasn't imagining someone else in my place, but sharing these vulnerable moments with me- Jane. I was enough.

"Can I..." I swallowed, breathing harder and harder from the numbness flushing down my legs and the anxiety filling up my chest. I closed my eyes, took a shallow breath, and pushed the question through my teeth, "Can I try something?" My palms felt swollen, wet, and beating. Why did I always have to be so ambiguous? Why couldn't I just say what I meant?

"What?" he asked.

"Just... something," I answered, looking at his chin now.

He took a moment to think it over, wondering what an appropriate response to my vagueness would be, and then parted his lips, "Okay." It was his vote of confidence in me. I could've wanted to do anything to him, but he trusted me enough to know I wouldn't hurt him. I wasn't a burden any-more- just a person.

"Okay," I echoed, blushing like mad, but I didn't want him to see me, so I told him to, "close your eyes..." which he did. He didn't even ask me why I wanted him to. He was just going along with it to make me happy.

Jonah's delicate face shined brighter when his warm gaze was curtained behind his veiny eyelids. His nose was a bit crooked, but not too much. His lips were fuller and his brows were thinner than James's. His hair, a curly mat of brown locks, spilled over his forehead and the sides of his face, framing his cheeks with tendrils. His jaw was round and there was a noticeable flab beneath his jaw, but these imperfections only made him more attractive. Just like I couldn't explain a great many things, I couldn't explain why so many people were attractive to me. There was no standard for beauty in the congregation. Those thoughts were considered immoral and lustful, so it was never discussed. The only person I knew was physically attractive was Superiorii Phorgiveness because women fled from his temptation. However, now that I've been living in the outside world for a decade, I know how ingrained these beauty standards are in people. The small things like crooked teeth, acne, scars, lack of a jawline, big noses, and odd complexions never really matter when you're face to face with a kindred soul. Weight, height, skin color, eye color, and hair color, texture, and length are all inconsequential. Little do people know, deviations from the norm are the most wildly attractive qualities to those that have seen your soul because it distinguishes you from the others. It's their light in the darkness which they flutter towards when they're lost.

I took up my fingers, trailed them through the air, pressed the tips to his jaw, gently out of fear I would crack his delicate face, and turned towards him. I rolled onto my knees, leaned forward, scrolled my fingers towards his ears, down his neck, and back towards the floor because I didn't have the courage to keep touching him. Why did my nerves always have to ruin things? His eyes stayed closed, though, not even flickering open out of curiosity, and I still had my chance to do what I wanted to. So, I stared at the space between the tip of his crooked nose and his medium lips, the philtrum, and focused on it as it approached me closer and closer. He wasn't leaning in, I was. I had my fists cemented to the floor for support as I inched my breath closer to his. I could see the fuzz on his cheeks dotted by petite pores. I could feel his exhales warm my top lip. His lips weren't parted and mine weren't puckered. It wasn't a romantic or childish kiss… I just gently pressed my lips against his, softly until it tickled, and a dam of guilt broke within me, flooding my mouth.

'What about Superiorii Phorgiveness? What about your loyalty to him? What about your love for him? I thought he was your one true love? I thought you were only going to do this with him? Are you this fickle? Are you this disloyal? It's no wonder why everyone hates you! What about your promise to the Antifasi? What about your fidelity to James? The Antifasi has seen what you've done! You will be thrown into the left furnace for it! Everyone will know! Everyone will be happy when they finally get rid of you! You're a portal! The Fos Terata are inside you! You will become one of them! You just corrupted Jonah! You just committed an impurity with Jonah! You just killed Jonah! You just killed Jonah!'

"No, I haven't," I moaned and with that I fled.

I don't know if Jonah opened his eyes when I started talking to myself or when he heard my feet running away or when he heard me shutting the door behind me or when he felt alone again. All I knew was that I felt a drowning, suffocating, murdering sense of guilt overcome me when I just thought about him. He made me feel like the terrible person I already knew I was.

C hapter Sixteen

I sat within the pew, trapped between James and Jeanette like always and forever more, writhing my conscience for whether or not I had damned myself. I didn't know what kisses were... I thought I invented them... but it still felt... wrong... Guilt stabbed its familiar claw into my chest- not guilt from my adultery, not guilt from my anxiety- guilt from knowing I was the portal causing so much unrest within the congregation. The Superiorii will soon sense my evil. The congregation will chant for my execution, no evidence needed. The congregation's logic was if the accused is being accused, then they're already guilty. It's no wonder why Superiorii Faithfull, despite his promotion of genital mutilation and inquisition-styled interrogations, was the popular member of the Superiorii.

He was a snake. They all were. The Superiorii were filled with deceit, treachery, ambition, and rage and Superiorii Faithfull had full control over Superiorii Depherence now. He threatened to execute Superiorii Depherence on the grounds of adultery if he didn't support his motions. How? Jeanette. Superiorii Depherence brutalized and raped Jeanette when he was still childless. She would damn him to the fire without a breath. Loudly, proudly, without mercy. Besides, there was little keeping Superiorii Depherence from the furnace anyways. In fact, most mothers within the congregation wanted to see him burn so badly they were willing to lynch him. A power Superiorii Depherence probably underestimated, considering his disdain and low opinion of women in general. Nonetheless, Superiorii Faithfull controlled him, thus he controlled half the Superiorii opinion.

Superiorii Depherence gave up his sermons to Superiorii Faithfull and the two of them barred my father from giving the few sermons he had. Superiorii Phorgiveness abstained to vote. The only authority we now had was Superiorii Faithfull's interpretation of an arcane book... I wasn't educated enough to realize the severe problem of having one person, or even a select few, with that much power over others.

I was so used to being powerless its different forms were indistinguishable.

I didn't know there was a world of people living their day to day lives with clean food at hand, clothes they chose to wear, and women with long, straight, short, or curly hair wearing it as they pleased just outside those boarded windows. I couldn't fathom a world so free. Torture and submission were natural. Even when I peeked a glimpse of that fresh world through my wildest dreams, I immediately felt guilty for wanting something supernatural.

How dare I not be content with what the Antifasi has given me? The safety he's provided? I deserved to be outside with the other rebel humans, cowering from shadow to shadow, hiding from his divine light. It would transform any of us into a Fos Terata if we so much as even grazed it. That's why we threw people into the left furnace if they touched the light without mercy- they were truly doomed.

That's what the Antifasi did to you if you touched natural light- even by accident. It was an offense that merited disfigurement. If you did something wrong within the congregation, like fall in love with someone you weren't forced to marry as a child, he took it as an offense that merited death. He demanded you be thrown into the furnace where you burned to death before everyone you've ever known and be transported into the land of the Fos Terata where you were then eaten by a swarm of diabolical creatures for eternity. No one was spared this fate- no matter how young you were. He was loving, though. He was a father to us all. He guided us down a righteous path to avoid incineration... even though he was the one who made up the rules. He gave us this lightless world to keep us protected from his curse. He provided food whenever he *could*, despite being all powerful. This was the best world he could come up with, despite being all knowing, and I, an impure, rebellious, ignorant, and ungrateful little girl... or woman... depending on if I'm being judged or controlled... was not content with what I had been given.

I was going to burn. I grew up knowing my fate. I never fit in. My mind wasn't disciplined. It wandered into original territories, developing opinions of its own. I wanted bad things. I knew they were bad, but I didn't understand why. Like kissing Jonah. I didn't accept what was good or bad at face value. I wanted to know why they were good or bad. Why couldn't I become a member of the Superiorii? Why couldn't I read the Den Amfisvito? Why couldn't I marry Superiorii Phorgiveness? Why couldn't I fight my father when he went on one of his tirades? Why couldn't I smother James in his sleep? Why couldn't I gut this thing growing inside of me? Why couldn't I just be at peace? Alone. Where no one would bother me or tell me what I could, or more commonly, couldn't do. On top of that... everything everyone considered good... I thought was bad. Marrying someone you hardly knew, being raped until pregnant, forcing women to dress in potato sacks from neck to toe, covering their faces in ash, throwing someone in the furnace for deviating from the norm or questioning the system of things, only allowing men to have power, nepotism, dictatorship, judging others for the sake of conversation, letting grown men beat and sexually abuse children. It was all disgusting to me. It's all disgusting to me. How could any sane person excuse such deplorable, vile, diabolical acts?

The answer is- when some book written by power-hungry men, claiming they were inspired by a higher being, is interpreted by other power-hungry men who say those acts are not only alright, but expected. And people blindly follow...

... and feed their children fear since birth to blindly follow in their place.

"Though I know none of you are committing the impurity of fornication," Superiorii Faithfull lied, he always suspected the worst of the congregation, but he started off the morning sermon with his lie anyways, "I wonder if you are committing this impurity within your mind... where no one in the congregation can see you... Though I know none of you are committing the impurity of adultery!" he roared, "I wonder if you are committing this impurity within your mind... where no one in the congregation can see you..." his tone calmed to that of a protective father. His signature warmth oiling his tone rather than drumming against it.

Repetition. What a useful tactic to ingrain your point into your captive audience. When I heard Superiorii Faithfull slam the word 'adultery' against the congregation, my heart turned into stone, taped itself against my chest, and weighed me forward. The guilt was getting worse... I had been living life as a numbed woman for months. This sudden surge, this trek down a nostalgic path, this overwhelming feeling of being wrong had become unfamiliar to my system. I had forgotten how to cope with it. Little physical signs were giving me away and if anyone cared to look at me, they would've noticed my guilt.

My chest was heavy. My lungs popped. My breaths were shallow. They couldn't fill the organs. They escaped through the holes and blew into my hollow stomach. The mouth of my stomach had been tied off. I could feel the knot tying itself tighter and tighter, crawling up my esophagus, reaching my lungs, tying nooses around them. My popped lungs were halved and hanging by their nooses. I could feel blood trickling down against my ribs, pooling in my belly. It flooded me. I tried to breathe, but my gasps were superficial. I was drowning. You could tell by my accelerated breath. My chest quickly, but barely rising and dropping. The air bubbling within my nostrils, teasing me with relief, but letting me suffer.

THE LIGHT WAS GOOD

I dragged my fingers over my knees, as discreetly as I could, and grappled at the edge of my seat between them. I grabbed so hard my fingers burned. The knuckles were turning a pale yellow, but the sensation was pleasurable. It was a luxurious relief. I pressed them against the chipped wood even harder until the skin around my knuckles felt like it was tearing apart and the bone would soon be exposed. I could feel blood pumping at my forehead, took a deep, hard breath, inflated my lungs, popped the nooses from them, and resurrected them. No more holes. I could breathe again. My chest was rising tall and dropping hard.

"... but you know who can see you?" Superiorii Faithfull continued with his onslaught, "The Antifasi... He can read your mind... He knows your thoughts... He watches what you do when no one is around and listens to what you think... and according to the Den Amfisvito... thoughts are as evil as actions, if not more so," he panned his gaze over the congregation, looking at certain people for flickers of time, "If you allowed seeds of lust... to grow in your mind... You will be punished by the Antifasi. Upon your death, your soul will be thrown into the world of the Fos Terata to be forever eaten by the Fos Terata since you managed to deceive the Antifasi's congregation your entire life. There will be no mercy. No end to your suffering. You will be swarmed and ravaged for the rest of eternity!" he slammed the pulpit with his hand, open palmed, and then softened his expression to reveal sympathy towards us. He cared about us. He wanted to help us. That's what he wanted to express. Was it calculated? I don't know. I don't care. He was still suffocating me.

My lungs were trickling with anxiety again. My stomach still felt hollow, so I tilted forward and wrapped my arms around it, remembering it was filled with a creature far fouler than the Fos Terata- James's spawn. I had committed adultery... I had allowed seeds of lust to grow in my mind with Superiorii Phorgiveness and harvested them with Jonah. Pressing my lips against his was adultery. I didn't have sex with him. My idea of

209

sex was rape, so what woman would want to commit adultery? But, I knew that blissful, surreal, passionate, heart beating moment was too good not to be wrong.

"Brothers and sisters..." he called out, looking down at the congregation assembled before him, asserting his dominance, but making us feel special with each glimpse he gifted us individually, "... physical purity is easily achievable. But, to keep our children protected from these lustful men who fail the Antifasi more than our sisters do," the women stirred a little and sat up, happy they were being acknowledged, "I say we rid ourselves of temptation... After a healthy baby is born, both mother and father should slice temptation from them and rid themselves of the evil thoughts... I know the women in the congregation are more than willing to follow this simple command, but are the men?" his chin lifted, "Your voluntary submission is indicative of your purity in heart," Superiorii Faithfull was clearly picking people out from the audience to look at for reasons unknown to me, "and likewise, your refusal is indicative of your impurity..." his chin lowered, "and you will be thrown into the furnace where the Fos Terata will eat the temptation from you along with the rest of your body."

There always had to be an ultimatum. That's the dialect of any abuser 'asking' you to do something. If you do this, then nothing will happen. If you don't do this, your life will either be ruined or violently ripped from you. And then their glimmer of false humility and kindness returns to their empty eyes, a horrific, deluded expression, and a smile to further prove how gentle of heart they are despite threatening death.

"As you can see, brothers and sisters," his left brow raised, leading him to my side of the room where he was now concentrating his stare deeper across us, "remaining physically pure and keeping our children safe is easy. What is pain in comparison to the Antifasi's love? What is a little pain in comparison to keeping our children away from impurity?" he swallowed, "What is a little pain in comparison to keeping our children away from these men?" he looked down at the pulpit, blinked, and within the instant, his stare crashed down upon my father, but smoothed back up towards the congregation.

The corner of my father's right eye tightened as he beaded at Superiorii Faithfull, though, it was too late. Superiorii Faithfull wasn't noticing him anymore. He was ignoring him now. His right nostril twitched and the corner of his mouth shrunk in towards the middle of his face to further tighten his hateful expression. For some reason, I felt his anger was geared towards me. My existence was a pain to him. My constant inadequacies, mistakes, flaws only proved I was mistake incarnate, my being was a mistake, and he knew it. He just put up with it. He should've killed me when I was born a daughter and not a son. He would've spared us both a lot of trouble.

My lungs had shriveled up and knotted together, dangling above the blackhole of my stomach which was sucking the air out of me. Each time I breathed, I was fanning the flames of my anxiety. An anxiety warning me of some unavoidable fate. The idea of an entire congregation watching me burn was too shaking to ignore. The vulnerability, my honest expression captured by judging, superficial eyes with no depth of soul, my screams, my cries, my begging heard by the soulless. Genuine feeling was an impossibility for those limited creatures. They had nothing in their minds except the upholding of convention and nothing in their hearts except their own indulgence. And these were supposed to be the last people who saw me alive. But, it was fitting... These were also the only people I could associate with while alive... For the first half of my life, they were the only people I knew. It only makes sense they should watch me die, too.

"Jane..." Jeanette whispered, *"... are you okay...? You're sweating..."*

I tore one hand from the pew, pressed the dry tips of my swollen, tingling fingers against my forehead, pulled them away, and swooshed the dripping beads between my fingertips away. I was dripping wet. My body was burning, my pits were soaked, pasted to my sides, and I could feel my neck both hot and cold from the steam emanating from it and the cool breeze blowing in from the boarded-up windows.

"*Stop seeking attention, Jane,*" James ordered, grabbing my shoulder and throwing me against the back of my seat, "*sit up and pay attention!*"

"*Is it the pregnancy, Jane?*" Jeanette asked, even softer than before. She didn't want to disrespect James's claim over me, but she was still nervous for the child's sake. Even if I was feeling terrible, as long as the unborn creature inside of me was still alright, everything would be as it should to her. Her attention, however, unnerved me, as did her disposition. I could tell she was risking James's wrath by persisting, but why should she care? Why did it have to be like this? James didn't have to control who spoke to me, in fact, what was his legitimate claim to controlling me at all? Because the Den Amfisvito said that's the way it was supposed to be? Now I was questioning the Antifasi again...

"*Jane?*" Jeanette insisted, wrapping her fingers around my arm, demanding my attention, but I, in my confusion, acted impulsively. I whipped a wild-eyed look at her and snatched my arm out of her grasp.

"*Don't touch me,*" I warned, feeling my lower jaw protrude further out than my upper to show off my bottom canine teeth ready to rip her throat out. The offense was apparent in the rings beneath her eyes, at the corners of her mouth, and from her slightly raised eyebrows. It said all too plainly, 'How dare you speak to me like that?', but instead of cowering and apologizing like some kicked puppy, I maintained my stance. 'How dare you not leave me alone?' Unlike her entitled stare, mine was that of a madman's. Unpredictable. She didn't know who or what she was dealing with anymore which, of course, unnerves anyone far too comfortable with convention. Especially if they've learned the rules of convention well enough to manipulate those who also abide by it, but little to nothing else. How was she supposed to intimidate me now? How was she supposed to dominate me?

With a bit of resistance on her part, she eventually turned her head back towards Superiorii Faithfull, but most likely not her attention, and did her best not to glimpse at me through her peripheral vision. She didn't want to incite a face-to-face 'scene'- she was far too used to having people swallow the cruelties she tossed into her friends' ears behind her victims' backs. However, when she turned, the reality of what had transpired crashed over me like a bucket of ice water and I began shivering uncontrollably again. The adrenaline was coursing through me, challenging me to run from my seat and keep running away from everyone, from this world, from my life. I had revealed too much of myself, too much of my opinion towards her. All I wanted to be was a specter, but somehow even that was too much to ask.

"*Stop that!*" James demanded, feeling my arm rivet against his, but no matter how hard I tried to freeze my muscles in place, to imagine Superiorii Phorgiveness's hands soothing them like before, I just couldn't. "*I said stop!*" he hissed, grabbing me by the arm far harder than Jeanette had, but still I whipped my arm out of his grab.

"*I can't!*" I growled back at him, which only made the shaking worse. I could feel my neck vibrating beneath my head now, bouncing my skull all over in quick jumps, but nonetheless I glued my psychotic glare tightly onto James's. I hated him. I wanted him and this child of his dead. He'd never even know how many times I've thought and dreamt of murdering them. It was one of the few ideas that made me happy.

He realized I hated him. I wasn't like any of these women, like our mothers, made from stone- emotionless and tolerant. I wasn't his little toy existing for his sadistic, narcissistic pleasure. I was a human being, a creature, capable of feelings, rage and murderous intent, and capable of executing her wants. Push me far enough. Do it. I'll kill you even if it means being thrown into the furnace because I'll burn with a smile on my face and the picture of your dead eyes on my mind. Do it.

After a pause, after a few moments of him staring me down, trying to reduce me, but failing, he spoke. "*The only reason,*" he began, with an authority in his tone that indicated he was more my father than my husband, "*I'm not choking you right now... is because I don't want people looking at us... but you'll regret this little...*" he twitched his stare from my eyes down to where my collarbones were hidden behind my dress and back up to my eyes, "*... whatever it is you're trying to do.*"

Superiorii Faithfull's voice was still humming away like white noise, an undertone, to James's voice. I just wanted to be unnoticed again. I was tired of this drama and was willing to do anything to get it over with. Including, which is what I ended up doing, keeping silent. Rage still crashed against my heart like the torrents of a storm blasting over bricked up dams, but my anxiety was raining over me. I tore my stare away from his, dropped my chin towards the floor, and accepted his threat without defense. Back then, it was only a minor fee in exchange for my mental seclusion. I needed to sort out my feelings and figure out what was going on inside of me, but it was an impossible task. It was like fixing a fallen and inherently flawed empire-when it was still on fire.

"If you have questioned the Antifasi's system of things..." Superiorii Faithfull continued, "... if you think the brothers and sisters in this congregation aren't good enough for your company..." my heart was injected with a fresh injection of dread, "if you have thought about committing an impurity, or worse! If you have committed an impurity already," I couldn't breathe anymore. My heart was choking me, my anxiety was gagging me, I was shaking. "there is no hope for you," his stare lingered over the left row, my row, and he was now trailing his stare down from the back towards the front, "You can't slice temptation from you," he pushed, "You can't throw the ideas out your head," he bashed, "You're poison," his stare was settling. "You're poison..." he repeated... looking at me, "... and when the Antifasi calls you to judgement through the Superiorii- he will condemn you. And you will be executed for having tempted his congregation," his eyes narrowed, his face tightened just like my father's, but then he looked away... leaving me to wonder... was he really looking at me? Or was it just my paranoia?

I looked towards the back of the congregation, trying to find Jonah in his usual seat, in the hopes that I could ask him how he felt about the kiss, but he wasn't there.

Before James could haul me to our room or Jeanette could slap me with whatever plotted retort she'd concocted throughout the sermon, I dashed from their midst, impulsively again, towards my safe space standing in the other row. Superiorii Phorgiveness. I was still shivering and drowning, but his hands were the medicine I needed to soothe me and my tempest waters down. I wanted to break and sob out one of those painful episodes where my stomach cramped from the pressure. If I did so in his arms, like I had as a child, I'd forget why I was even crying in the end. I needed him. I wanted him. I wanted him so badly I ignored the fact that he was still standing beside his wife and I, now a married 'woman', was approaching him, and just him, a handsome man, imprudently.

I swallowed, took a breath, and lunged the words, "Superiorii Phorgiveness...?" out of my throat. I stood a few feet away from him, fidgeting my fingertips against one another, peeling the loose skin from them, but I still did my best to look at him- even if it was just his shoulders. Both the Phorgiveness and the Depherence families turned to look at me, more so because the Depherence family noticed me standing behind the

Phorgiveness family, waiting, rather than because I called, but I had my gaze cemented on Superiorii Phorgiveness. The words, 'What is it?' were coldly tattooed upon the majority's eyes. Except for Superiorii Phorgiveness who, after all this time and humiliation, still looked at me with the same gentle warmth I remembered from before. "Can I..." I inhaled, feeling the adrenaline bubble up higher and higher, but I held my breath to keep my voice from shaking and through the exhale said, "Can I speak with you please?"

I thought I hid the tension in my tone quite well considering how highly strained it actually was, but apparently-even with my best efforts- he could still tell I was scared. The warmth disappeared and was replaced with concern. But, considering all the vulnerable episodes I'd had with him since childhood, he probably recognized my rickety disposition ham-handedly tied together for the sake of keeping composure and came to my aid unwaveringly nonetheless. None of the others really picked up on my tension, so I think the latter was probably how he noticed I wasn't alright. "Of course... J-..." he almost stumbled as his attention rushed from them towards me, "Sister Loyaltie," he quickly corrected, despite still being wrong. I was Sister Virtew now, not Sister Loyaltie, but it was a minor mistake that I'm sure the others didn't weigh too harshly. He took a few steps towards me, enough to let me know I had his full attention, but distant enough to avoid suspicion, "Do you need to confess something, sister?" he asked.

The others were still looking at us, but he was innocent to their attention. I think he was just as excited to talk to me as I was to talk to him. Whatever warm chord we had winded tightly around our souls was fastened the same number of times on both sides. But, this wasn't good enough for me. Having to rush through little superficial exchanges instead of divulging the pains I'd gone through in only two, almost three, long months, the guilt burning me, and my confusion that only he could sort out would've been an insult to our relationship. "Yes,

I do, Superiorii Phorgiveness," I answered, trying to stir up the courage necessary to ask him if we could meet in the old room again, but the moment was fleeting. I had remained silent for a second too long. It was his turn to speak now.

"Oh, well then, my sister," his voice hushed and stiffened, for the sake of propriety, but it still remained as toasty as a crackling fire on a winter night, "in that case, you should meet with me this evening where others can't listen in on your private affairs…" his head shifted slightly towards the onlooking crowd he left behind. They were hardly being discreet about their interest, but his defining, resolute stare from the corner of his blue eyes were enough to make them work harder at keeping up appearances. "… you know where the Superiorii meet to study, right?" he asked, which made my heart stop. This wasn't going to be an official matter, now was it?

"Yes…" I answered, hollowly.

"Well then," his tone was changing, his eyes were softening, his countenance was returning, and that same hint, hint, wink, wink disposition, that little secret vibration, had returned, "you know where to find me…"

In the old room.

C hapter Seventeen

I wandered off after dinner. No one noticed my disappearance, but I was sure they eventually would. For at least one night, though, I didn't care. I'd face the consequences at James's hands and Jeanette's critiques, but that night I was going to breathe. Nestled up against my old sanctuary's furthest corner, waiting for my Superiorii Phorgiveness to walk in, close the door, and hold me again. I was going to enjoy my happy moments without fear of what was to come.

When you confessed or approached the Superiorii, no matter the concern, your husband had to be present. If you were discussing your husband's severe abuse- rape, of course, was not considered abuse- which could've ranged from him choking you unconscious to him breaking your bones, he had to be present. If you, the wife and then woman and then human being, didn't please your husband, you were considered a proud demoness who held her opinion above the Superiorii's. A woman with loose morals- the worst thing a woman could be. Your name was kept in their records along with a rough transcript of your conversation, exaggerating your comments or fabricating your statements as proof you might be a portal within the congregation. Usually, no official punishment came out of it, but the Superiorii would discuss the matter with your husband and demand he better control his wife... You could only imagine what a monster like that ended up doing afterwards...

I didn't tell anyone where I was going. I was tired of my private life being prodded and examined for flaws, people looking at me, trying to piece me apart, to see where they could 'help' me. I wanted to be left alone. I wanted my life and my secrets respected. Should I tell Superiorii Phorgiveness about my kissing Jonah? It was one of my secrets, but it's a shared secret between Jonah and I. Who knows if Jonah told anyone about the kiss, but I highly doubted he did. Otherwise, the furnace would've roared our names during dinner. I kept the secret buried.

"Evening, Superiorii Phorgiveness," I rehearsed in hopes I wouldn't break down in tears or freeze up at seeing him in such an intimate setting again, "How are you? How have you been? How's Juliet and the baby? Do you think her husband is going to be a good member of the-... no, no, no... too forward... It's not my place to ask such a thing..." I muttered, fiddling with the tips of my fingers as my toes bounced the heel of my foot up and down against the stone floor. "Evening, Superiorii Phorgiveness," I tried again, "How are you? What's been going on in your life since-..." I paused, "no, no, ugh..." it was far too impersonal. I wanted a balance between normalcy and vulnerability. I wanted the balance we used to have peppered over with my newly founded maturity and capacity for critical thinking.

I was no longer the ignorant, stupid child constantly asking him questions and incapable of coming up with thoughts of her own. I was now a broken woman... with disturbed thoughts... and questions... and perspectives on the congregation I knew he couldn't tolerate. My innocence was gone. There was nothing left of the former me. He was still my beloved Superiorii Phorgiveness, nostalgia incarnate, a figure from my romanticized childhood, a supposedly better time in my life, but I was just a stranger to him. I was even pregnant... how could he hold a pregnant woman in his arms? It was so... wrong...

I realized how much of an adult I had become. From the moment I married James until then, I considered myself the same girlish Jane immune to adult consequences, but it wasn't true. There's always someone there to tell you what you can and cannot do based on arbitrary, personal standards. My parents 'disciplined' me based on their standards and controlled my activity. Now these strangers, these Superiorii, could 'discipline' me based on their arbitrary, personal standards. The only thing that differentiates between being treated as a child versus being treated as an adult is who's doing the treating. I was a pregnant, married woman... who happened to be around thirteen... infantilized to where I didn't know how pregnancies, or how one managed to get pregnant, worked. I didn't know what James was doing to me all those nights, but I knew it hurt and I felt ruined. I was a weak child incapable of protecting herself from whatever anyone wanted to do to her. Marriage? Between two consenting adults in love? It didn't exist. I was a child bride forced to marry someone in his late teens/early twenties who wanted a child immediately. The irony. No one noticed he already had his child. But, my pregnancy was the defining feature of my adulthood. I was like all the other mothers in the congregation- cold, stone-like. I was no longer the little girl crying at night in Superiorii Phorgiveness's arms. I was a soon-to-be mother.

"Jane...?"

I jumped. I was so caught up in my thoughts I hadn't noticed Superiorii Phorgiveness walk in and close the door behind him. He rushed with urgency in his step when he noticed the emotions swelling up in my face. The surprise ripped the balance from my heart- fear, woe, shock consumed me, "Jane, sweetie..." he comforted, kneeling before me. He brought his hands over my arms, wrapped his palms around them, brushed them up and down like before, and his fingers just washed over my arms rather than constricted them, "... is everything alright?"

I elevated my chin a bit, swallowed whatever I had stuck in my throat, licked my lips clean of the collected goo from having kept silent for so long, and loosened up the muscles in my jaw. I needed to speak now. This was my moment to maturely and clearly explain. I looked at his eyes, those same blue eyes that used to cheer when he'd laugh or sharpen when he heard my father and Superiorii Faithfull argue, and felt everything inside me crash hard against my stomach. "No..." I cried, doing my best to maintain composure, but failing. My voice clapped the roof of my mouth and I broke down, crying, collapsing into his chest, hoping he'd wrap his arms around me which he did.

"What's wrong, Jane?" he urged, "Are you feeling guilty again?"

I sobbed even harder, feeling the ribs in my chest burn. He still knew me so well, remembered what pained me as a child, and was consoling me. Superiorii Phorgiveness brought one hand from my spine up to the back of my skull and held me in his soft palm. He shushed me, lolled me, he even dragged my bum onto his crossed legs and rocked me back and forth gently. "Breathe, Jane," he calmed, "breathe in..." his chest rose, "... and breathe out," his chest dropped. His exhale blew against my scalp- reminding me he was alive. He was another human being, not a figment of my imagination, who was acknowledging my existence and respecting my pain.

"Why..." I cried out, long and exhausted, "... why..." I couldn't finish my exclamation. Saying 'why' just felt so good. It captured everything I meant.

"What is it, Jane, my dear?" his voice was far warmer than before. It was heated honey rolling down a wooden bowl, pooling within its center. I could hear his heart beating hard- I felt it punching my ear. He could feel my pain.

"Why..." I heaved, "... why can't I just live my life the way I want to...?"

Silence. What could he say? A member of the Superiorii. A hypocrite. A snake. A monster just like all the rest.

"Well," he started, "how do you want to live your life, sweetie?"

"Without James!" I almost screamed had it not been for the reminder looping in the back of my mind, telling me to keep quiet otherwise the others would hear, "Without Jeanette...without my parents..." and that's when something in me clicked and my tongue, like clockwork, whipped out every natural thought that came to mind, "without the congregation, without anyone telling me what to do, how to feel, how to think, without the

Antifasi," that one felt surprisingly good to admit, "without the Den Amfisvito, without this thing inside me, without all this pressure! Why did James have to hurt me! Why did I have to get *pregnant!* I'm going to be a mother! *A mother!* Why do I have to live according to everyone else's rules- including the Antifasi! Why do they have a say in what I do with my life! They're not smarter than me!" I was never stupid. They convinced me I was stupid. It's easier for someone to make themselves feel smarter by making someone else feel stupid instead of working towards being the smarter person, "I'm not stupid!" my heart felt lighter, "I'm not stupid! I was never stupid!"

"I know you're not, Jane," he soothed, softening his voice, hoping I'd follow suit, "I never thought you were stupid. I always thought you were the smartest person in the congregation."

"I know you did, Superiorii Phorgiveness," I choked, trying to soften my expression, but I wasn't relaxed. I was agitated. Why should I pretend to be something I wasn't for the sake of someone else's comfort? "But they did," I could feel my lower eyelids trembling in anger, "and I hate them," my words came out like warnings- I was ravenous and losing myself. "I want them all to die! I want them all thrown in the furnace! I want to watch them burn! I want to hear them scream and smell the flesh melt from their bones!"

"Jane!" Superiorii Phorgiveness gasped, "How could you say something like that?"

"How could the congregation make me marry James? How could they let him beat me? How could my father scream at me? How could he threaten me? His daughter! His only daughter! And my mom just stood by! She did *nothing!* Because he's the head of the household? Why? Why? Oh! Because the Antifasi made men better than women- I hope the Antifasi burns! How could people tell me what to do? *What to do!* I'm forced to do what I don't want to do just because everyone tells me it's something I should do! But why? What's the point? What's the point to morning sermons when they're all the same? What's the point to having almost nothing to eat? What's the point in talking about others? Isn't that supposed to be an impurity? Why doesn't anyone punish Jeanette or Aunt Faithfull? They spread lies! Why do they just punish people who commit fornication or homosexuality? At least they both wanted to do it- what's the harm in that? They're not hurting anyone! No one even loves their husband or wife in the congregation! How can they? They were forced to marry them! As *childten!*" I boarded the same train of thought I was on before Superiorii Phorgiveness surprised me, "James hurt me! He hurt me so much and for so long! And he was supposed to hurt me! I had to accept the pain because it was expected of me! *Expected of me!* I'm a child! *A child!* And I'm pregnant with *another child!* Why couldn't I be left alone? Why can't I be left alone! Is that too much to ask? According to the Den Amfisvito it is! Wanting to be alone means you're prey for the Fos Terata and if someone within the congregation is alone too much, the others gossip about them- saying they've already been taken! That they're portals! What sort of love is that? If the Antifasi is supposed to be all loving, then how come the congregation doesn't get thrown into the furnace? How come it's just the people who fall in love that are burned? I can't even be alone with a boy without feeling like I've committed some terrible impurity! Just alone with a boy, doing nothing, but talking! *How come?* Adulterers? Fornicators? Men who love other men, women who love other women? They're just trying to be with someone they love! *Someone they want to be with!* And yet they're considered evil while the gossipers and judges and those that rush to the front to see an execution and the men who abuse children and abuse their wives are all considered pure! If that's what the Antifasi wants- then the Antifasi isn't good or loving! He's evil! He's evil! The Antifasi is evil and I want him thrown in the furnace! I want the Fos Terata to forever eat him! I want him dead! I want him to suffer! He's evil! He's evil! He's evil! How come no one else sees that! How come no one else questions anything! Why do I have to feel bad for just questioning things! If I can't question something, then that's bad because everything should be questioned- especially if it controls my life! *But no!* I have to keep my head down, keep thoughts to myself, control what I think because the Antifasi will torture me if I don't! Well, then throw me in the furnace!" I screamed, looking up at the ceiling, "Reveal me! I'm a portal! *I'm a portal!* Throw me in the furnace and be done with me! I hate you! I hate you!"

"Jane, please," Superiorii Phorgiveness hushed and I lowered my voice again- shoving my fears away. It felt good being honest. Raw expression is delicious. It liberated me. I wasn't going to let the fear of someone overhearing me get in the way.

"And then the Superiorii," I scoffed, "they're the only ones who can interpret the Den Amfisvito... They're the only ones with all the power... But, they disagree... And you have to choose who's right... but if they can't agree on interpretation, then how come they're the only ones who can interpret? No one here has a voice! A mind of their own! Everyone follows what the Superiorii say and when they disagree, they take the lesser of two evils! No one thinks- maybe there's a better way? Maybe we can work towards making the congregation more peaceful? A place where we can actually be happy! Instead, they follow the loudest people and burn the thoughtful ones! The questioners! The ones who think about solutions to these problems! They're burned!" I drew a deep breath in, "I hate them! I hate the Superiorii! I hate the Antifasi! And I want to die! I hate my life! I hate being here! I don't want to live like this," I broke down, "I don't want to live like this, I don't want to live like this, I don't want to live like this..." I choked out quiet sobs into Superiorii Phorgiveness's chest, feeling my tears squeeze through squished flesh around my eyes, burning my heated cheeks on their way down, "I don't-..." I choked, "... I don't want to live like this," I brought a fist to my eyes and pressed down against the eyeball hard, trying to free my face from tension, "I don't want to live like this," I stressed through my gnashed teeth, "I don't want to live like this," I choked again, rubbing my fist against my forehead, "I want to die! *I want to die!* I want to die!"

A child chanting for her own death. That's what my childhood world did to innocence.

"Please, Jane..." Superiorii Phorgiveness tried, but his voice was trembling. I looked up, blinking to clear the blurring tears from my eyes, and noticed tears streaming down his cheeks. His eyes had reddened, his blue eyes more vibrant, looking straight at me. "... I'm so sorry," he whimpered.

"Why?" I asked. It wasn't his fault- in fact- he was my beloved Superiorii Phorgiveness. The only one who understood and took care of me. The only person I felt loved by.

"I-..." he paused, looking away to consider what he was about to say. 'Should I stop now? Should I tell her? Can she handle it?' These were the questions probably running through his mind, but I mistook the pause as him composing himself to continue speaking to the girl he was in love with. It's the warped reality a teenage girl dupes herself into believing for the sake of momentary happiness. "I should've told you..." he stammered, "I *tried* telling you! But... it was a story... of course, you didn't understand it... but I should've- I should've told you *plainly!*"

"Told me what?" my heart accelerated. Was he finally going to profess his love? We could sneak off every night like before and sleep together! I could kiss him more deeply than I'd kissed Jonah! I could kill this spawn inside me and have his child instead!

"You're not trapped, Jane..." he sighed, but afterwards he hardly breathed again. His chest was still, "... none of us are trapped... The Superiorii lied to the congregation... and even to themselves. There is no such thing as the Fos Terata or the Antifasi... The Den Amfisvito isn't the Den Amfisvito... It's called another name in the outside world..."

Silence. He was waiting for my reaction, but I didn't know what to say. "What do you mean?" I asked. I thought this was another story or an exercise in imagination, but his severity undermined those possibilities.

"... I mean..." he swallowed, "... my dear, sweet, darling, Jane..." he looked at me, but clenched his eyes in shame, a trickle of tears rushed down the folds, "if you leave the congregation, if you break through one of the windows and escape, you'll be free of all this... The Antifasi doesn't exist... He won't come after you. The Fos Terata don't exist... They won't eat you. You'll find people like us, but healthier. They have food, clothes, medicine-..."

"What's medicine?"

"Something you eat when you're sick to get better," he answered, "they don't meditate to the Antifasi for health... They learn what makes a person sick and then learn what that person needs to eat to make that person feel healthier... People your age, children, aren't married let alone impregnated. They play with other kids and since their world is so big, even if they can't make friends with some kids, there's always more kids they can try to be friends with instead." He had to be mocking me. These ideas were unfathomable. I thought I was dreaming or Superiorii Phorgiveness had gone crazy because... a good world outside? Everyone told me the congregation had the best situation of all humanity. We've been blessed with the underground. We were protected within our stone walls. The Antifasi kept us safe on the inside. They told me never to go outside because I'd be eaten by the Fos Terata. And here... Superiorii Phorgiveness was telling me my imaginations were realities, "People still control what you do in the outside world, but they're not as powerful as the Superiorii are here... They won't cut off your genitals or kill you over sex or make you shave your head..."

He further explained the world outside, but I couldn't process any of these stories. He was explaining a great cosmic truth to a simple mind or particle physics to a child. It just couldn't register. "How do you know all of this?" I emptily asked.

"One night... when I was a little older than you... I was studying the Den Amfisvito... Your mother was with me," my ears rang and my heart stopped. Why would my mother be with him? They knew each other this entire time? "She was my best friend... If it was up to her, she would've married me, but I just..." he sighed, "... I just can't... can't love anyone... romantically..."

"What does romantically mean?"

"It means you don't like them as a friend, but as someone you want to have children with..." it was a poor explanation, but he had to relate it to familiar concepts for me. I remained silent. There was a wild, needy look of curiosity blistering in my eyes. "I only loved her as a friend... despite our different feelings, she still snuck into the Superiorii room when I studied... I taught her how to read... and I told her everything I learned... That night I found a small door with her in the Superiorii room that led to an old library filled with books which hadn't been touched in decades and a window without boards... The Superiorii would eventually send me through this door and out the unbarred windows to ask local bakers and grocers for leftover bread or potatoes. Other times, we had to steal food. They sent me, your father, Superiorii Faithfull, and Superiorii Depherence when we were still small enough to fit through the door, but despite that, I was the only one who wondered why we were lying to the congregation. There was an entire world outside our windows, a better world than this one, yet we were telling the congregation the opposite and scaring them. That's when I stopped believing in this nonsense... I thought about running away because... the stress was... is... too much... but I couldn't leave without your mother. She was my friend. But, she was too scared to leave...

"I told her everything I knew, all the Superiorii's secrets, including what the meat is made from, but she was still too scared to leave... I told her the world outside promised freedom for us, but I think it was the change that scared her. She was used to her surroundings... She was used to the torture... and didn't want to leave behind her mother... because her father beat her... So, we stayed... We spent the rest of our childhood reading the old books from the library at night. I loved stories with questionable heros- she loved romance stories. The ones about love," he explained, "her favorite was Romeo and Juliet. She loved Shakespeare," nostalgia spilled in his eyes, so I refrained from interrupting him... even though I was wondering what the meat was made from. He didn't interrupt my heated rant, so I wasn't going to interrupt his stroll down memory lane, "I named my daughter after your mother's favorite story..." he clarified, "... but," he sighed, "of course, there came a day where we had to grow up... Your mother was married off to your father who was older than both of us and I had to wait a couple years to marry a girl your age... And I had a child... but the process of having a child was just... something I didn't like..."

'Neither did I,' I thought.

"The act itself wasn't natural to me... I could've gone my entire life without doing what I did, but I had to because... the congregation *expected* me to... When I die, I need someone to take my place as member of the Superiorii... Juliet's mother was disappointed she'd given birth to a girl, but I was more than happy to have a healthy child... Juliet could marry my successor, so succession wasn't impossible through a daughter... And I never had to... do anything with her mother again... Besides..." he swallowed, "I love my daughter... She's another reason I stayed, but another reason I wanted to leave. I didn't want her growing up here, suffering like your mother. I wanted Juliet to escape... to have a different life... but I was so busy with matters of the Superiorii while her mother raised her into a distant young woman... And now..." he thought, blinking tears away, "Juliet has no problem with our world, so why tear her apart from it?" he rushed, convincing himself rather than telling me, "I'd only be traumatizing her if I told her about the outside world."

"Then, why did you tell me?" I asked.

The bearded man's aged gaze swaddled me for a moment. He settled his hands on my shoulders, leaned in, and pressed his lips against my forehead. I was shocked. My heart both dropped and floated away. Had my beloved Superiorii Phorgiveness finally professed his love for me? He knew the secret existence of kissing, so were we sharing one mind? Maybe we had a piece of each other within our souls. He parted his lips from my forehead and noticed how flushed I'd become, so he brushed a hand over my cheek, pinching it a little, and then smiled. "You're not like her," he explained, "you were raised by a different kind of woman," in my mind, I disagreed, but I said nothing. He stared at me with such love and warmth and tenderness. I couldn't help feeling accepted. He did love me! "Do you remember how we met, Jane?"

"Of course!" I assured him, nodding through my shock and growing a smile, "I was playing in this room and you showed up, sat me down, and started telling me stories. You told me I could keep visiting you every night and I did."

"Do you remember who showed you this room in the first place?"

"Yes," the air was knocked out of my lungs once I realized, "mother told me... I could go play in this room whenever my father was angry... She said it was a room no one would bother me in." I looked up at him with knitted brows and waited for his explanation. His confirmation that what I realized was true.

"We wanted you to grow up differently," my heart sunk... They're the reason why I grew up feeling so wrong, "We didn't want you to accept this world like Juliet or support it like Jeanette and her little friends, pleased with the way things are, incapable of thoughts or opinions of their own. We wanted you to be like us."

I suffered so long for nothing. Why hadn't they told me before? I would've been free from all this... misery... "Well..." I tried, collecting my thoughts, "... doesn't that mean I can leave? I'm still small enough to fit through the door, right?"

"You are!" Superiorii Phorgiveness smiled, alarming me with his enthusiasm, "You'll just need to find someone wearing blue and one of these things," he drew a star into the dust on the floor, "on their clothes and tell them you're an orphan. They'll take you to a place better than this where they'll feed you and clothe you and let you play with other kids your age."

"But..." I tried again, noticing more and more problems with that plan, "... I don't want to leave without you."

"Oh," he moaned, "I'm too big to fit now, Jane."

"Can't you squeeze through?"

"Maybe," he thought, "but I'm too old to do anything in that world. I can't just go up to a man in blue and be treated the same."

"But I can't leave without you," I said more excitedly, "I need to leave with you or I won't leave at all!"

"But you can't live here, Jane- it's killing you!"

"I won't leave you!" I cried, "I'll never leave you! Never again!" tears swelled in my eyes and before I knew it, I grabbed him by his bearded face and pressed my lips deeply against his, parted them from his, gazed at him heatedly, and tried kissing his lips again, but he pulled away. "Why!" I screamed, "I love you, Superiorii Phorgiveness! Why didn't you marry me! I wanted you to marry me! But you just stood by as I married James! Why! Why don't you love me!"

"Jane," he tried shushing again.

"Why don't you love me!"

"I do!" he tried, but I was cracking- I couldn't keep anything in anymore.

"Not the way I love you! I want to have children with you! You just love me as a friend!"

"No! I love you as a daughter!"

"I don't want to be your daughter! I want to be your wife! I want to mother your children! Not *his!*"

"No, Jane," his grip over my shoulders tightened. "Look at me, Jane- no, look at me, Jane," he ordered when I tried avoiding his stare out of anger. "Jane," his voice became as baritone as Superiorii Faithfull's, and as authoritative, but it retained its sincerity. I looked up at him with tears dripping from my eyelashes, streaming down my cheeks, and noticed how serious he was.

"What?" I choked out after he took too long to say what he seemed to have trouble with saying. Whatever it was, I reasoned, it couldn't be worse than learning the Antifasi and the Fos Terata aren't real, my world is false, and I could've escaped marrying James.

"Superiorii Loyaltie isn't your father, Jane..." he finally said, "... I am."

My skin blew up like a balloon.

He exhaled and I could tell he felt relieved. It was probably something he always wanted to tell me during our nightly visits and now I knew. Superiorii Phorgiveness was my father. "Superiorii Loyaltie," he explained, "couldn't get your mother pregnant... He married your mother years before I married my wife and I had Juliet years before you were born. But, what James did to you, your father did to your mother- for *years*. And the few times she was pregnant, she was so scared of miscarrying that she miscarried. So, one night, your mother and I were sitting in this room. We came here after we outgrew the door to the library. I was holding her in my arms as she cried about Superiorii Loyaltie, the same way you cried to me about James, and it broke my heart. All she needed was a healthy child and he'd never touch her again. So, even though I never loved your mother in that way, and despite never liking the process of making children, I offered to impregnate her since I already had a healthy child. And she agreed. So, I... *helped her...* that night and nine months later, you were born."

"You hurt mother...?"

"No, of course not," he asserted, "I didn't hurt my wife either. Your father, James, and a lot of the men in this congregation just like violence and hate women. I did my best to be gentle and asked how they felt during the act. Your mother was shocked at how painless it was when I finished-..."

Superiorii Phorgiveness went on about how happy he was when I was born and how he wanted to be there for me the way he failed to be there for Juliet, but I couldn't listen to him. The truth blew up in my face and my ears were ringing. "So... Juliet is my sister?" I asked hollowly, remembering the lustful thoughts I had of her.

"Yes, Jane... half-sister," he corrected.

"And, Superiorii Loyaltie... *isn't* my father," shivers nibbled at my shoulders while saying this. I hated Superiorii Loyaltie for the screaming, the humiliation, the fear he built in me, but the idea of him not being my father anymore was just... wrong.

"No," Superiorii Phorgiveness answered.

He was doing his best to soothe me, brushing his claws up and down my shivering arms, gazing at me with his clear, dead eyes, but this time- it made me shake even harder, "Please stop," I snapped. He stiffened at my turning on him. He tried saying more words and more words and more words, but all I could think was- all those nights we were together... all those nights I spent crying to him... he could've saved me... he could've saved me from Jeanette... from James... from malnutrition... from humiliation... from this pregnancy... but he kept my salvation from me... He lied to me. I could've escaped. Now, I'm trapped. I'm stuck in the underground with... a lying mother and a new father, doomed to repeat their history.

I had impure thoughts about my own sister... I fell in love with my own... father... I wanted to have children with my own father... All those nights I spent lying in bed awake beside James, daydreaming I'd have a son with Superiorii Phorgiveness for comfort, came at me like a pack of wolves and tore me apart. I was so confused... Everything, absolutely everything, was a lie... I felt humiliated, used, and stupid for not realizing it sooner. At least my former father was honest about his cruelty, but Superiorii Phorgiveness? All he had to do was tell me the truth and none of this would've happened. All my mother had to do was run away with him and I could've had a life outside the underground. But, they didn't.

"Jane?" he called, but I couldn't bear to look at him. Just his presence reminded me of my shame. "Jane?" he called again, brushing the back of his finger over my cheek to catch a tear I hadn't noticed rolling down. "Are you okay?" I said nothing.

There were no words in me- just screams and silence. I stood up, letting his arms fall around my legs. I felt them tighten around me, but he loosened his grip when he noticed my stare heat up. My mouth was parted, my jaw hung by its muscle, and I only raised my gaze slightly to find the door handle. I clicked it, remembering the night I ran away from Superiorii Phorgiveness, and swung the door open. But I still couldn't leave...

... there was someone in my way.

After my eyes adjusted to the blackhole of the hallway, I realized who it was, "Superiorii Faithfull...?"

C hapter Eighteen

Jonah told Superiorii Faithfull about our being alone, the kiss, my feeling of otherness, and since then, Superiorii Faithfull had been attentive to my whereabouts. The grown man followed me down the hallway... in the darkness... hunting down my impurity... stalking me... waiting to catch me in the act... waiting in the next room while I cried to Superiorii Phorgiveness... listening to every word... remembering every consonant... Superiorii Faithfull was an insatiable man hellbent on his dictatorship. A sadist. Someone reaping pleasure from inflicting pain on others. He didn't want to dominate the congregation as a group. He wanted to control the individual- from the oldest to the youngest- including pregnant, little girls.

I never blamed Jonah for telling. He was a little boy. His psyche was overloaded with guilt and terror, just like mine, but he witnessed his father burned before a crowd. My father was the man who damned him... whether you think of Superiorii Loyaltie or Phorgiveness... They both damned his father... The congregation chanted for his father's death... His father died looking at his wife and son watch him burn without emotion... Then, Joel started raping him... using his father's death to silence him... and when the Superiorii found out about the rape, who knows what sort of interrogation Jonah went through, "Did you try to stop him? How? Do you really think you couldn't fight him off? Why didn't you scream? Why didn't you come to us sooner? Why did you just keep it to yourself? You know the Antifasi sees everything, Jonah! He sees everything!" It's no wonder why he told... The fear of being caught was a spear through his chest and to pull it out, the truth had to be spilled. My father and Superiorii Phorgiveness, or the other way around, weren't called in to vote.

Jonah was lynched in private before the morning sermon. He burned silently. It wasn't the afterlife which frightened him, but his mother. He didn't want to die looking into her disappointed eyes, so the privacy, the loneliness, comforted him. And despite his confession, he was burned in the left furnace. By having his first kiss, Jonah committed adultery consensually and was found guilty of sodomy with Joel as well. If you've committed an impurity, you are an impurity, and you can't rape an impurity because they want to commit impurities. That was the congregation's logic. If you're guilty of one crime, you're guilty of all of them. That's why he wasn't in his seat. By the time Superiorii Faithfull slammed his first underhanded accusation against the congregation, against me, that soft, nervous boy, my first official kiss, was dead.

"Have you lost your mind!" my father barked down in Superiorii Faithfull's composed face. My father's face was a hunk of red, uncooked, dripping meat with a hole punched through it. He had blasted in from the hallway, exploded the door from its hinges against the wall behind it, and charged at Superiorii Faithfull who was seated across from me in the Superiorii room.

The table we sat at wasn't the grand, Arthurian table I imagined the Superiorii assembled around. And the room wasn't a strong expanse of knowledge, huge for the Antifasi's word, and a humbling force for those who stepped inside. It was a small room with a dining table... and the Den Amfisvito was resting on the tabletop... a tiny book with faded print on its cover... Just tossed... It was all so little... The room, the book, the table- their power... Tiny men, screaming over tiny problems, reading from a tiny book with tiny power, wanting to scare me... a tiny girl... who could still fit through a tiny hole in the wall and escape...

The library was behind Superiorii Faithfull. The entrance was blocked off by light plywood resting against the wall, unnailed, inviting me to move it.

Superiorii Depherence escorted my mother from our

family's room into the left furnace room. Superiorii Phorgiveness had been sitting in the left furnace room since the night before as I had been sitting in the Superiorii room. They were still alive. Their executions couldn't take place until they were made into examples. They were the reasons we needed genital mutilation, Superiorii Faithfull's regime, and paranoia within the congregation. Can you trust the Superiorii? Can you trust your wife? Is your child really your child? Their door was unlocked. They could have run out, ripped the boards off a window, and climbed into their new lives, but they didn't. Their trials were scheduled for that morning sermon. They only had an hour to live, yet they spent that time waiting. Obeying. They were already examples... of conformists.

Upon hearing the door explode against the wall, Superiorii Depherence rushed from the furnace room into the Superiorii room, alert and sweaty, fully expecting to see my father bashing Superiorii Faithfull's head against the stone floor.

"My wife- my wife and daughter!" My father was restraining himself. His arms were yanking through the air autonomously for Superiorii Faithfull, but each time one swung out, it hit an invisible wall before him. Superiorii Faithfull's eyebrows twisted, 'Do it,' his face challenged, but my father didn't dare. He never did. *"You're only doing this because of what my father did to you!"* my father exclaimed, "And I'm sorry, Jacob, I'm sorry he used you as an alternative, I'm sorry I didn't do anything when I walked in on you, *I'm sorry!* But, how can you take your anger out on my wife! And my *daughter!* She never did anything to you! *She wasn't even alive when it happened!"*

"I accept your apology, *Superiorii Loyaltie*," Superiorii Faithfull interrupted, emphasizing my father's proper title, "but no one in the congregation, neither man nor woman nor child, can escape the Antifasi's wrath when they commit an impurity... even members of the Superiorii family... We can't forgo the Antifasi's wrath lest we experience his wrath ourselves."

"Yes, I know that, Superiorii Faithfull." My father's eyes, like an unhinged animal ready to maul his enemy, bulged out of his skull. All the barbarism he already had difficulty handling was now shooting from his tear ducts like steam from a tea kettle. He gnashed his rotted teeth at the little man and slipped each word carefully through them, imitating a civilized man, "But would you mind telling me, *Superiorii Faithfull*, what impurities *both* my wife and daughter have committed?"

My father was valuing me for the first time. I wasn't his mistake, but his daughter. He was calling me his daughter. Every time he said it, it reaffirmed my value. All his abuses, his screams, his torments, the psychological trauma of never being wanted seemed to change into this heavenly mixture of honey and lavender, healing the burns. I was happy. My father wanted to protect me. He believed in me. He wasn't angry at me for being accused of an impurity. He was angry at Superiorii Faithfull for taking me...

... but good feelings don't last long. He was hellbent on defending a wife and daughter which weren't even his; and the daughter he suddenly felt such passion for was actually his childhood friend's daughter he ignorantly raised as his own. Dread consumed me until I was swallowed up into the dark void of anxiety. My senses dulled in anticipation. Superiorii Faithfull telling both my father and I our new truth.

I thought Superiorii Faithfull was going to outright tell him I wasn't his daughter. Start with the most shocking news to undermine my father's will and lead the conversation without challenge. Watch him suffer with the truth as he watched him suffer beneath his father's breath. But, even when revenge was served before him on a platter, Superiorii Faithfull took his time to prepare the cutlery, "Very well, Superiorii Loyaltie," he began, "I am an honest man," though somehow, despite his apparent honesty and attention to the dishonesty of others, that adjective didn't ring true, "but you should sit down because this is a long list... I don't think any man has character enough to remain standing in the face of such charges against his wife and…" he looked over at me without a trace of true feeling, but rather an accusatory look of, 'How could you do this to him?' and continued, "… daughter… Superiorii Depherence," he motioned, "close the door please," which he did, "and come sit down with us."

After Superiorii Depherence sat down beside Superiorii Faithfull's left side and my father chose the seat at the head of the table, one seat away from me, on Superiorii Faithfull's right, Superiorii Faithfull began batting off charges, "I'll start with your daughter…" he said, barely needing a moment to recall my sobbed confessions.

His first point was, "She expressed hating you, James, the congregation, the Antifasi, and the gift inside her… She expressed wanting to murder everyone," I could feel my father's shock, but I hated being talked about as if I wasn't in the room. Give me a moment to defend myself, give me a moment to speak! Why wasn't anyone looking at me? Not even my father cared to look over at me- me- the very person whose actions were shocking him. And why was I being talked about? Why was I among their midst instead of with Superiorii Phorgiveness and my mother? Even though I didn't know for sure, in my stomach, in my mind, there was a stone, an idea, a small pebble that kept growing bigger and bigger, but in no rush. It gradually grew at a steady, not hastened, but not slow, pace. They were going to die. They weren't going to have a trial… It wasn't like this whole charade was my turn and then I'd be thrown into the furnace room and one of them would have their turn to sit with the Superiorii. They were already judged. But, if that's the case, then why was I getting a trial? Why wasn't I sitting with them?

The wrath which roared eternally behind my father's eyes turned to smoke. The firewood turned to ash. "When…?" he asked, still not broken, just hurt. His voice coiled at the end of the word, wincing from being further told about how his daughter truly felt about him.

"Last night," Superiorii Faithfull answered, coldly, but professionally. He was like a politician- restraining his fake sympathy. His capacity for sympathy, let alone empathy, was as real as the Antifasi. "She also expressed an interest in killing herself and questioned the Den Amfisvito, the Antifasi, and the Superiorii's right to govern."

"What?" He exhaled the word out without strength, but his fingers had minds of their own. The tips were pressed hard against the wood and they were bent in sharp angles, pushing out the rage I'd always known him for through his fingertips.

"Yes, I'm sorry to say," no he wasn't. He was more than glad to say, "she even admitted to being a portal..." My father said nothing to this. He continued to ignore me, not out of disappointment, but because, to them, I wasn't in the room. This was a conversation between them that didn't involve me- I was just there as a sort of fixture. An adornment. My being there gave them the gossamer of being fair in judgement because I could, in theory, speak for myself, though I wasn't supposed to.

"Why isn't James here...?" my father swallowed, "Why isn't James here?" he repeated with a little more presence.

"Because, Superiorii Loyaltie..." Superiorii Faithfull's eyes narrowed in his puzzlement, "... this isn't a confession... this is a judgment..." he leaned in, "You're a Superiorii of the congregation who so happens to be her father, not the other way around. You need to be present to hear out her list of crimes, along with her mother's, and Superiorii Phorgiveness's-..."

"Superiorii Phorgiveness!" my father cried, sweating, "By the Antifasi, what has *he* done?"

"I'll tell you if you refrain from interrupting me..." he asserted to which my father slumped back in his chair in resignation. How were his wife and daughter linked to one of his childhood friends? After clearing his froggish throat, Superiorii Faithfull continued, "Jane also admitted to being in love with Superiorii Phorgiveness and wanting to have his child instead of James's," something in my father flew out of him, "She was alone with Superiorii Phorgiveness last night. I found them in a closed room... in the dark... alone..." he explained quickly as my father sat up, still hollow, seemingly ready to ask something.

"He didn't...?" my father shook his head, absently, "He didn't..."

"*They* didn't, Superiorii Loyaltie," Superiorii Faithfull emphasized, "and I don't know. Considering how she's already had intercourse with James and is pregnant with his child, it's difficult to say unless they admit it... but I don't think they did..."

"Why?" my father asked, but Superiorii Faithfull shrugged the question off and continued.

"She also committed an impurity the night before last with a boy from the congregation... Jonah..."

My heart dropped. There was this scream inside my head, it wasn't a desperate one, but a howling, yet restful wail that sounded more like a shrieking yawn than anything. It wouldn't let me think of anything except the single image of the furnace door- immobile, closed, but menacing nonetheless. And Jonah was in there.

"The homosexual's son?" my father's shoulders squared, "How do you know?"

"He confessed."

"Where is he?"

"With the Fos Terata."

"*With the Fos Terata?*" my father shrieked, regaining his usual manner, "Why didn't you drag me to *that* judgement, Superiorii Faithfull?"

"Because, Superiorii Loyaltie," the robust man threw back my father's name like a brick, "Jonah confessed... It wasn't a judgement- it was a release. He couldn't live with himself. And the congregation couldn't live with him. He was a portal. Have you forgotten your education?"

"What did he say?" my father demanded to know, "What did the-..."

There was a knot in my throat and my eyes were already watering, flooding. I couldn't restrain a drop cascading down my cheek, but I quickly swiped it. What about the connection Jonah and I had? Those warm, tender eyes accepting me, understanding me, welcoming me into his world. We knew each other. He was the first person I felt open and comfortable with. And now he was dead. Because of me.

"He said..." Superiorii Faithfull slowly began, tilting his head to the side, beading his cautionary eyes at my reddening father who was only growing more volatile. I couldn't gauge what emotion my father was chasing after- woe? Rage? A mix of both? He was jumping between a pool of tar and a lake of fire. The tar was dripping from his bones, filling him with a weighty depression, while the other was breathing fire out his pores- exciting his monster. "... he was sitting in the same room I found Jane with Superiorii Phorgiveness... The same room Superiorii Phorgiveness found Joel with Jonah... And Jane walked in. Nothing was arranged, they just happened to be there that night. But, they both stayed, together, alone. Do you think it's right for a boy and a woman, let alone a married one, to stay in a room together alone?"

"I'd trust my wife to stay alone with a boy," my father arrogantly answered, wanting to spite Superiorii Faithfull, but there was silence. I thought Superiorii Faithfull was going to tell him about Superiorii Phorgiveness, but he didn't. He kept staring at my father until he looked down at his interlocked fingers and licked his thin lips.

"It's never alright for one person of one sex to be alone with another person of another sex... No matter the age, no matter the relationship. It is wrong. It is an impurity."

It sounded like mothers couldn't be alone with their sons. Never once had I been alone with my father, but this was merely coincidence and I didn't think there was anything wrong with being alone with him unless he was angry. The reason for the rule was because they thought if a man and a woman, or a boy and a girl, or maybe even a baby and a baby were alone together, then intercourse or sexual exploration would occur. But, I spent countless nights with Superiorii Phorgiveness and never once had I so much as kissed him on the cheek. I had been alone with Jonah and granted, yes, I barely kissed him, but I hardly call that sexual exploration let alone intercourse. They were the perverts assuming every little interaction led to sex. But then again, projection is a powerful guide and people judge according to their character.

"I'm really starting to question your competence as a member of the Superiorii, Superiorii Loyaltie," Superiorii Faithfull admitted, sucking a bit of the already sparse air in the room, but he continued on, "Jonah confessed to having intercourse with Jane."

So, that's the word for when you press your lips against someone else's- *intercourse.*

"*What!*" my father snapped, "... Oh, Antifasi!" he called, looking up towards the stone ceiling, "Why? *Why!* How could she do this to you?" he raised his open palms up, but then filled them with his forehead. He bowed his head in shame and covered his face.

Was it really that bad? I didn't know. I wasn't informed of my crimes. I had no idea what they were talking about. I assumed what I was being accused of was what I had done. I knew I felt guilty. I did commit an impurity. I kissed Jonah. However, what I would come to learn a month or so later was that I was being charged with a far harsher crime. Maybe Jonah would've been spared had he not misspoke or if Superiorii Faithfull hadn't registered it the wrong way?

"So, you now realize why Jane is being judged?" Superiorii Faithfull asked and my father nodded, still holding his face. He wasn't breathing. He was holding his breath. The short, robust man sat back in his seat, his posture still as erect as ever, and he, in his perceptions, graciously offered my father a break, "I'll give you a moment," he said.

"No," my father exhaled hard, a bubble of drool popping from his lips. He snorted the snot dribbling out of his nose, a little too loud, and rubbed his steaming forehead against his palms. "What about my wife?"

"You need a moment, Superiorii Loyaltie," Superiorii Faithfull insisted.

"What about my wife?"

Another silence. Brief. Everything about Superiorii Faithfull's countenance changed from 'I'll do you this favor' to 'very well, suit yourself.' The robust man sat up, rested his elbows back onto the table, shrouded the lower half of his face with his interlocked fingers, and cracked his neck, "Joan committed an impurity," he explained, "She had intercourse with another man."

My father let out a groan, but maintained his shaking composure. His fingers were a pale yellow from the skin twisting closer and closer to the bone and harder against his skull. His lips were wrinkled, but raised, his nostrils flaring, but the tip of the nose sharp, and his cheeks were trembling. He pressed his palms deeper into his eye sockets and stirred them softly at first, but then thrashed the meat around his face. No one said anything. He brought his face up, dragging his palms down his cheeks, collecting the fat towards his nostrils, and pulled at the lower eyelids with his fingers, revealing more of his emptied gaze to Superiorii Faithfull, "Was it with Superiorii Phorgiveness?" he asked through his hands.

Superiorii Faithfull nodded and my father gave a quick nod of understanding.

He reburied his face back into his palms, but his expression was much colder than before. My father was in the eye of the storm. That's when numbness takes over to settle down nerves, but there was going to be another wall coming. It was useless denying it. No matter how hard a sailor tries to avoid lightning, he's still trapped within the storm. He could sail north, south, east, or west, but in any which way- he was going to get hit, "When?"

"I must insist, Superiorii Loyaltie, take the moment," Superiorii Faithfull urged, but my father's expression completely changed, flushed, resigned, composed, and emerged. He looked at the robust man across him and maintained his drunken stare, allowing his arms to drop down before him.

"I'm not here as her husband, Superiorii Faithfull," my father informed him, coldly, "I'm here as a member of the Superiorii. Now. When did the accused commit their impurity? Did one of them confess?"

"Very well," Superiorii Faithfull pursed, leaning in closer to my father, "The accused committed one impurity, to my knowledge, before Jane was born. I know this because I heard Superiorii Phorgiveness admit it to Jane when she was professing her love for him."

"So, Superiorii Phorgiveness told my daughter he's in love with my wife and not her?" my father reasoned, doing his best to show he could handle the situation.

"No," Superiorii Faithfull corrected, clearing his throat once more. "Superiorii Phorgiveness..." he began, clearly having a hard time not scrolling his stare away from my father's, "... He told Jane he's her father."

Lightning struck my father and he was lost to the sea. Drowning before us, already dead, a ghost returning to his watery grave.

His eyes were pinned open. He tried keeping the hurricane from his eyelids, but failed. He couldn't breathe without sobbing, so, instead of bearing the shame, he raised his palms to his face and tried burying his face again. His arms gave out and he collapsed onto his forearms, though, his back heaving in and out from the burn. Was he crying? I couldn't tell. The idea was unfathomable, but it wasn't until I heard a familiar, choked out squeal that I realized the unfathomable was possible. I tried comforting him by pressing a hand against his arm, but he rejected me. He tore his arm away from me and let my hand hang in the air.

"My sermon today will concern their impurities," Superiorii Faithfull assured, "Why it's wrong for people of opposite sexes to be together and why the congregation should rid temptation from their bodies..." he was going to use the death of my parents to further his agenda... "... and they'll be thrown into the land of the Fos Terata to suffer far more than you are right now, John." Superiorii Faithfull pressed his hand against my father's other arm, but he tore it away from him, too.

"What about me?" I choked out, hurt, frozen, but what an inappropriate question to ask. How dare I speak after everything I've done to my father? Kissing a boy, being another man's daughter, expressing how I felt to someone I trusted in private. The betrayals were innumerable and now! Now I had the audacity to ask about my fate? My birth parents had just been sentenced to death, but there was still no reason for me to *speak*. Did I forget I wasn't a member of the Superiorii? Or did I forget I was a woman? A heretic...

"For your impurities, we must cleanse the congregation of your presence," Superiorii Faithfull answered, "but you have a precious life inside you. A gift from the Antifasi... There's nothing I value more than life, Jane..." his stare was so steady. His voice rich enough to swallow, "...so, until your child is born, we'll keep you here, guarded by the Den Amfisvito, protected by the Antifasi's wrath. When the child is safe from you, we'll burn you in the left furnace."

C hapter Nineteen

They didn't lock the door. I wasn't tied to a chair or chained to a wall. Yet, I didn't leave. I wasn't supposed to move. The metal stakes of obedience kept my tombstone of a body secured to the ground. Subservience was instilled in me. Don't move. Don't breathe. If you don't exist, you can't make any mistakes, so I pretended I was a disembodied consciousness studying the human world. A ghost. I still wanted the congregation to like me... It didn't feel right for them to hate me. I wanted to impress them. Show them how intelligent I was. How capable of critical thought I was now. They not only drilled a sense of blind obedience in me, but also a longing for their approval. I wanted them to notice my capability to validate my existence.

If I was praying for their attention, the thoughts scratching at my head and chest, thinking of ways I could show them my newfound worth, then I wasn't worthy of whatever respect I wanted. If the only way my character could be validated was through another's opinion over me, then that character was built on sand and would wash away. Granted, I was fighting against the urge to show my 'strength' or sense of 'inner peace' because I knew they were cruel, corrupt liars, but I still felt submissive to them. Feeling something despite knowing better is such a thirsty, toxic trap that sucks the body of energy. I was still immature. Now that I could've delighted myself with an inkling of personal progress, the sentiment was tainted with the strain of putting on airs so others would notice my achievement. I was objectifying myself. I was nothing more than a failure before. Now I was trying to show off my trophy. I was more than willing, craving, to show the very same people who destroyed the first version of me this new version I had replaced myself with. I was a child, a pregnant thirteen-year-old child bride, who didn't know the first thing about figuring out her own head- let alone what 'maturity' and 'wisdom' meant.

While the sermon was conducted by Superiorii Faithfull, and the remaining official member of the Superiorii was sitting, watching, I was thinking one thing. How would the congregation react to my death? Would they cry? Are they noticing my absence now? Are they worried about me? I enjoyed the idea of people concerning themselves about me. My existence was noticed and accounted for. I wasn't as invisible as I'd always felt. I was an actual person to these people rather than a stock figure meant to fill the background and disappear. Replaceable.

I was such a selfish child.

But, I think all the pain I derived from my childhood, the childhood I was deprived of, served to fuel my developing maturity and wisdom now. Maturity and wisdom only follow those who had the critical mind to make sense of their pain. It's an art- an underrated practice within a world that values loud opinions over quiet thoughts. *Why are you contemplating when you should be acting out?* The message screamed from every show, every false friend. The only reflection people care about is the one in the mirror. Even me at times. If I hadn't examined my pain, I don't know where I'd be... The madness would've destroyed me. It still destroys me- the shrieks, the screams, the smell of burning flesh, and all the what if's, but I can't think about that... It's best if I just reason out my lessons learned and implement them into my future, but to recall the details is a task too daunting. I really can't sometimes.

I sat so close to freedom. The little door resting. No one was watching me. I wasn't waiting for the perfect chance to escape. I was obeying. I was so close to my biological parents. We could've escaped together. As a family. They weren't locked or chained in their room either. They were waiting. We could've lived together- poor, hungry, and destitute, but we would've been alive. And none of us would've been alone. Completely alone.

     This idea didn't hit me then, though. I think that's what I hate most about reflecting over my past- those missed opportunities which seem so clear now. How could I have been so ignorant? Why wasn't I smarter? More insightful? Maybe if I possessed Superiorii Phorgiveness's knack for intuition, the idea would've struck me at the perfect time and I would've saved my parents. I could've rushed to their door, barged in, told them to run away with me, and they would've impulsively escaped with me. Imagine if I still had them... Imagine if I had someone to remember the past from a safe distance with, someone who understood where I came from, someone who doesn't pity me when I talk about my childhood. I can imagine all I want, but the reality is they're dead. My parents are dead. They're all dead.

     My only consolations are the reasons why those plans might not have worked. The door would've been too small for them. It wasn't even a door; it was a hole in the wall. They would've never been able to fit through. But, I could've crawled through. I could've climbed out, ran to a man in blue with a star on his chest, dragged him to the underground, and he could've saved my parents. He could've called the fire department and broken through the wall. But, that plan doesn't work either. There wasn't enough time to reach an officer, have him believe me, and wait for the fire department. Instead, the officer denied my story until the city found out. But, even if the officer had believed me, even if the fire department blasted through the wall, what if they fell in love with the congregation? The congregation was created by outsiders... Rational people like the officer and the fire department... Not the hypnotized or brainwashed or indoctrinated or abused... It was made by free people... What if they fell in love with the congregation's power?

     There had to have been a way to save them. There are so many options in the world, so many paths untaken, unthought of, that just one, or even a couple, should've worked. People say you learn from your mistakes and that's true. I'm incredibly analytical now and problem solve with ease, but I would've much preferred to learn a different way. There are several learning methods. Why was I stuck taking instruction from my mistakes?

The shark of a thought circling my mind was how the congregation would've reacted to my death. The classic notion. People who are unloved in life thinking they can watch mourners show them love in death. I didn't consider how I would process my parents' death. Or if I could process their death... I just wanted to know how others would process mine.

I suppressed all thoughts surfacing about Superiorii Phorgiveness. Everything I dreamt of, everything I wanted from him. All those dreams of him holding me in his arms, fathering my child, marrying me, running away with me. Those memories were slimy hands knotting my intestines to my heart. I kissed him on the lips... I confessed my undying love to him... He now knew... It wasn't a matter of swallowing down the idea and moving on. Denying reality as it would be. He knew the disgusting lust I held buried in my breast and now I had to deal with it. I was so confused, but I didn't want to deal with it. I wanted to pretend he never existed. His execution was convenient in making that want come true.

My mother, on the other hand, didn't come to mind. Periodically, yes, she was someone I thought of for a blimp of a second, usually whenever I thought about Superiorii Phorgiveness, but she wasn't someone I meditated on. Her death seemed so far-fetched, something implausible, impossible even, it didn't seem so pressing to think of her gone. The same concept applies to Superiorii Phorgiveness. I couldn't imagine them gone. I thought they were somehow, someway, going to save themselves from that fate. I thought I was going to see them again.

That's why I thought about my death. My death was always far more plausible to me than the death of those I've loved.

Superiorii Faithfull's booming voice was the backdrop

to my racing thoughts. It was muffled, indistinct, but present. Maybe if my door was open, I could've listened in on his sermon, but I wanted to bask in my loneliness. This was the first time I was alone during the sermon and it was comforting. Solitude wrapped me in a warm blanket. Sometime later I heard the scuffling of feet, the pace of one set reminded me of my father's usual step. The one I'd feel anxious upon hearing behind or in front of my parents' door. It made me tense up. I feared they were coming after me, but I relaxed knowing my father, Superiorii Loyaltie that is, was probably in no mood to see me. The other set of feet probably belonged to Superiorii Depherence, but I couldn't distinguish them. The door across from mine squeaked open, no sound was made, no voices heard, but there were even more shuffling feet- softening as they furthered themselves away from my room and towards the congregation. After a minute or two, Superiorii Faithfull's voice began booming again, louder this time. More passionate. More zealous. I still couldn't distinguish what he was saying, but I didn't care. Whatever was going on in their world didn't concern me, I had my own world now. I was finally separate from them. All of them.

The prying thoughts of wanting to show my new character dissipated into hatred. How dare they make me feel like I need their validation? How dare the Superiorii make me believe they were better than me? It was disgusting. They were disgusting. Their arrogance, their pride, their ability to deceive. Why couldn't I be as calculating? I wanted power, so I could defend myself from people like them. I wanted to attack them back, make them suffer. I was so much weaker than them, though. They had people backing them. They hunted in packs. I was alone at best. I was a little girl, a runt, wanting to kill a congregation of grown people. A little girl versus grown men. The helplessness scratched at my throat, rising and dropping as the raging currents waved beneath them, but I rejected myself. I wasn't going to let myself cry. I gnashed my teeth, punched a wall, slammed my fists against the table, kicked my legs out, ran around the room screaming. I didn't do any of that, except for gnashing my teeth and kicking my legs out, but that's what I wanted to do instead. That's what I thought would've made me feel better. I thought it would've made the world fairer towards me. It didn't, of course. Reality was still reality no matter how hard you dream.

The idea of burning was more comforting than horrifying to me. Horror was giving birth to the thing growing inside me. The only life these people cherished. The unborn. I wonder if my child would've thought for themselves and been executed for it. It's apparently a genetic flaw. Its life wouldn't mean very much to them, then. Once it was born, it would've suffered like its parentage. But, how could they keep it from me? How could Superiorii Phorgiveness lie to me? Of all people, my beloved Superiorii Phorgivness? All those nights together, all those moments of vulnerability, all those rants against my father, he could've told me. The opportunities were ample. My mother hardly spoke to me, hardly protected me. Of course, she never told me. It would've required a lengthy conversation. She could've saved me from this hell had she ran away with Superiorii Phorgiveness, but she was weak. She was selfish enough to birth a life in this tomb. She knew firsthand what they would do to me here, yet stayed. She let them break my mind, marry me off, rape me, impregnate me, and now execute me. She could've at least prepared me for what was to come... But, no- instead, they trapped me here...

I couldn't wait to hear them scream. I wanted to hear them suffer as much as I had. They threw me into this world. They let the Superiorii feed me guilt, anxiety, frustration, self-hatred, and they let them starve me. They let them shave my head. They let them steal my childhood. And now, I wanted to hear their lives ripped from them like mine was ripped from me.

Superiorii Phorgiveness didn't scream, though.

After Superiorii Faithfull finished, there was a grand shuffling of feet, a stampede even, making their way towards the furnace room. They were all congregated outside my door and one of them accidentally fell against it. I could only imagine how excited they were to watch my parents burn. The drama, the aftermath, the conversation, it was titillating. They'd have plenty to talk about for the next couple of days, or weeks, to come. 'Jane's child was probably fathered by Superiorii Phorgiveness!' It was something I could easily imagine them gossiping over. Who cares if it's at the expense of someone's life? If it wasn't theirs, they didn't see how it could be wrong. Solipsism is blinding and the majority of those people, if not all of them, had their eyes gouged out. They didn't see how it could've been them in my parents' place. They felt entirely removed from the situation. Those shallow animals...

Nothing was said. Nothing special. It was quiet. I knew the furnace door had opened because its roaring was louder than before. Gasps followed. Shrieks, screams, but none of them belonged to either Superiorii Phorgiveness or my mother.

I had entered an alternate reality as a wanderer. He wasn't dead to me. She wasn't dead to me. There was nothing to mark the event. I'd never see him or her again, neither his tender face nor her corpse, but I hated them so much that in that moment I didn't want to see them again anyways. However, I didn't want them dead forever either. What was going on? Who was going in? My mother or Superiorii Phorgiveness? Did one of them already burn? Were they both still alive? I was cemented to my seat, facing the wooden door, beading hard at it to see through, but I couldn't. Was solitude worth it? And then I smelled it... burning flesh...

'What's going on, Superiorii Phorgiveness?' I pled. He was sitting in the chair to my right, looking at me with those warm, blue eyes. The tender gaze I always felt accepted and welcomed in. 'Are you dead now?'

'I don't know... ask me tonight, Jane,' he replied.

'I don't want to speak with you anymore, though,' I confessed, looking away from the apparition, 'You lied to me... You're no different than all the others.'

'Do you really feel that way, Jane?' he asked.

'Yes...' I answered, feeling the bacteria of regret grow in my chest with every word uttered, every second passed, '... I don't want to see you again...' I don't know why we push those we love away. And I don't understand why those we love don't see the pain they've caused and fight for our relationship. But, the apparition respected my wish and disappeared.

It was Superiorii Phorgiveness. He died first. I know because once the fires died down, they burned my mother over his ashes. And I heard her shrieks...

She wailed and screamed and begged for a quicker death. She wanted mercy. Throw more wood over the fire, set the flames higher, shoot more gas in, let her burn faster. Her screams carried through the halls, scratched against my eardrums, and made other women scream, too. People were fainting, children were crying, men were vomiting. My emotions weren't a spectacle. I wasn't screaming out in pain, clasping at my heart, yelling out in heartbreak. I was silent. I was in shock. My eyes were bulging, red, my mouth gaping. I couldn't fathom what was happening. My heart stopped. My blood froze. My mind went to sleep. My ears were the only things working. They helped me listen to my mother's final screams for help. She was dying... She was being killed. Once the smell got worse, the screams stopped, and I fell over.

I'd never get to see my mother again... What did that even mean? I never got to see her in the first place, but she was still my mother. The woman who gave me life. She was dead. My mother was dead. I heard her die.

I lied on the floor, convulsing, shaking, paralyzed from

helping myself back up. Immobile except for spasms and reflexes. I remembered Superiorii Phorgiveness's tender touch, the way he'd always rub my arms whenever I shook. I remembered when my mom picked me up from the floor when I had my first period. What was I supposed to feel? I felt betrayed. I felt angry. I felt confused, but I also felt trapped, brokenhearted, shocked, traumatized. I felt like some creature was ripping out my organs and filling me with sand. I let out one screaming sob, all hacked up and bleeding, it tore through my throat, and then I went to sleep. I fainted.

I was in my seat again when I woke up. There was a plate of food before me. It had bread, moldy potatoes, and a slab of meat on it.

"Go on," James said, standing over me, grinning this empty smile that made his eyes glimmer out of excitement. His sick fantasies were going to be indulged. He was taking pleasure out of this scene. This warped foul scene he was trying to push on me. I thought he was just happy to know I had suffered and was going to die soon, leaving behind his coveted son. I had no idea what he was trying to do to me. "Eat, Jane," he insisted, "You must be very hungry." There was something ominous about his command. Had he poisoned the food?

There was no one else in the room. The Superiorii were in the main room eating with their family. Talking as casually as they had when Jonah's father died. James and I were completely alone, so he could do anything he wanted to me. No one would've cared as long as he didn't kill me. Only the Antifasi had the right to kill me. Even though his congregation had to do the dirty work and kill me for him. James was free to beat me, rape me, choke me into unconsciousness, anything he wanted, he was free to do it. I was his prey. In essence, nothing had changed between us except the longevity of our marriage.

I kept my silence and stared down at the plate before

me. The fork and knife laying on both sides of it, waiting to be used. I remembered watching my mother hover her fork over her food... She was just playing with her food. Letting time pass by. She wanted dinner to be done and over with, so she could go back to bed, on the floor, and lie awake while my father slept. She wasn't like the other mothers, those cold, hard women with stone faces. There wasn't a hint of deprivation or emotion behind their faces. They were hollow. My mother was miserable. She had lines around her mouth and eyes. Every morning her eyes were swollen. She was human.

Why couldn't I have realized this sooner? Why couldn't I have been more grateful? I could've had a relationship with my mother. We both suffered at my father's hands, we could've taken solace in one another. She could've been my friend. But, it was too late. She was dead. They killed her.

I didn't want to give James the satisfaction, but my feelings were too powerful. I didn't know what to make of anything. Too much had happened in only a day and I needed to be unresponsive? I wasn't made from stone. It wasn't in my nature to be unfeeling. I wasn't heartless. I was only a little girl who had, within a day, found out her father wasn't her father, the man she was in love with was her father, everything she was taught was a lie, both of her parents had kept her prisoner in a world that tortured her, and they were both brutally killed... Over a lie the congregation was living in...

I gripped the edge of the table, trying to restrain myself, bit my lip, breathed harder, but nothing worked. Nothing ever did. Whenever I wanted, or rather needed, to cry, I just couldn't restrain myself. It was like a demon possessing me. I didn't want it inside me, but it wasn't asking for permission. My eyes were watering, but I still hadn't broken down. I, at least, had that much strength left in me.

"So, you know, then?" James said, nearing his face towards mine, lowering himself a bit just to further trespass on my personal space.

I swallowed the knot growing in my throat and struggled through my feelings to say, "Know... what...?" but I didn't look up at him. I kept staring at the food because I knew if I moved my eyes, especially upwards, tears were going to start dripping from my eyelashes.

I felt so used. I always felt used, but it was matched with my idea that I was meant to be used. Now I know better. The congregation had subjected me to the degradation of being a blind follower and I, the girl who thought her defining feature was being different, was just a conformer.

"What the meat is made from..."

"No..." I answered, biting down on the word. Leave me alone, James. I don't know what game you're playing at, but please don't bother me. I could feel my lower eyelids quiver with the rest of my now shaking body. It wasn't hard, but enough for James to notice.

"You think I'm going to hurt you..." he said, closing the bridge of space between our faces, "... don't you, Jane?"

I refused to answer. What more could he possibly do to me? Or do again to me?

He took one of his short, pudgy fingers and dragged it across my cheek, catching a tear cascading down. His touch repulsed me. I didn't want to be touched. I never wanted to be touched again, but especially not by James, so I tore my hand from the table and whipped it at his. "Don't..." was the most I could muster through the pool of courage now flushing out of my chest. My voice quivered at the end. I was an animal taking a step back from its predator. It was enough to let my predator know he still had power over me.

James was incensed by my audacity. His eyes burned against my face like my father's had and I flinched away from him. I didn't think James would touch me. But he did. He grabbed my skull and slammed my face into the meat before me, its juices now bubbling inside my eyes and nose, burning them. He was shoving my face into the food like an owner shoves his dog's face into its mess. "Don't you *ever* touch me again, Jane!" he threatened, "Ever! *Do you hear me?*" he screamed in my ear, but I was still moaning, crying through the shock. Why couldn't I just be left alone? I tried answering, nodding, but his grip was too tight for me to move my head and my mouth was pressed too tightly against the plate. I didn't know what he wanted from me when he was the one keeping me from answering him, but I guess it was another rhetorical question. He tightened his grip around my head and shoved it harder into the food. I thought he was trying to crack my skull. But when he gave my head two good shoves into the meat, he let go and I sprung back in my seat, still crying, but doing my best to rub the meat juice out of my eyes and nose.

"Now eat the meat!" he ordered, but I didn't want to. My tears and mucus stained the flattened chunks lying all sponged out on my plate. *"Eat it!"* he barked, hanging his arm over the back of my chair to warn me that he would do it again. When I felt his arm shoot off the chair, the movement itself shaking its wood, I reflexively took up the fork and knife.

"I'll eat it, stop, I'll eat it!" I begged which made him stop. He was the unquestionable power. James leaned over, moving back into my peripheral vision and then centered his face right in front of mine.

"Good," he smiled, his eyes were still empty, but proud. He was such an insecure person. His instability was what made him cruel. He wasn't a sociopath like my psychologists classified him. He was just a boy. And in that society, in this society, boys who lack confidence and don't have control over their emotions are excused to behave cruelly. There was nothing that made him do what he did. He was just allowed to be cruel. "Eat up..." he taunted, bringing his body towards my side, leaning one hand on the table and the other on the back of my chair, "...

I'm sure you'll want your father inside you again..."

The memory of my mother playing with her fork lingered like an undercurrent, the thought of eating a slobbery slab of meat was repulsive, but what James told me didn't quite register. "What do you mean...?" I asked.

Inside me? The only thing inside me was this creature James poisoned me with, but how could a person be inside me? Let alone my father. And again? It was that part which baffled me. I shook my head to let him know I didn't understand and he let out a sigh. I was ruining his fun. I was ruining his jokes. Now he had to explain.

"The meat, Jane," the pride in his eyes excused itself and was replaced by the most obvious hint of contempt, "Do you know what the meat is made from?" I shook my head, looking up at him as he towered over me. I was caged in. "Your parents," he answered. I still didn't understand. And he noted that from my expression. "You've never wondered how the congregation always has meat after an execution?" he pressed on, "It's because when someone is burned, we collect their charred flesh from the furnace and serve it on a plate... The congregation is eating your mother and Superiorii Phorgiveness... We swept up their remains and put them on plates for people to eat... And once you have my son, we're going to eat you, too... And I'm going to ask for seconds... And I'll feed you to-..." my body shook harder and harder to a point where I couldn't hear James anymore. It didn't make any sense, but when I thought about it- everything fell into place.

That's why Superiorii Phorgiveness didn't want me to eat the meat. He knew. Everyone in the congregation was a cannibal... Mother knew, too. That's why she didn't want to eat the meat either, but she still ate it when the Superiorii pushed her. They were making her eat a human being... We ate the people we knew... And I ate it, too... and mother just let me... I ate a person... and not just a person- Jonah's father. Jonah ate his father...

Jonah...

Those big, brown eyes. The fireplace of a gaze which warmed me, a freezing traveler. His presence was my cottage, his stare was my blanket, and he had enveloped me within his soul. Was I in love with Jonah now? What did his death even mean to me? His murder... "What about Jonah...?" I muttered, thinking aloud.

"Oh, he's in there too, I think," James answered nonchalantly, inspecting the meat, but reality's last claim severed itself from me. I was lost within my mind. I thought James was the Antifasi taunting me. All of this was done in his name after all. Everything was a lie. People were being murdered and cannibalized over a lie.

"Jane," James called, but I wasn't responsive, "Jane!" he called again, grabbing me by the shoulder and slamming it against the shaking chair, "Eat the-...!" but my fist... The one clutching the knife... It flipped the knife at his touch and when he slammed me against the chair, I slammed the fist against his chest. I didn't think about it. My mind was gone, so my body, along with all my feelings, was free to govern itself.

I looked at James's bleeding chest where my fist still clutched the knife inside him. I ignored his exasperations, his trembling, and pulled the knife out only to stab him again, and again, and again. He couldn't scream. He was gasping, sobbing, doing his best to stop the blood from gushing out, clasping his hands over the wound, crying out, silently from the horror, but nothing worked. He collapsed on the floor, unable to stand from fear, and I stood up, brought my hands gently onto his, and moved them from his chest. His expression softened. He was looking at me with pleading eyes, begging me for help, "Jane..." he grunted, clutching onto my now bloodied hands, but I maintained my stare. Zoned out. Ghost-like. I was his angel of death.

I leaned in close to his face and said... "Now you know how I felt..." but he didn't understand. The anxiety, terror, powerlessness, hopelessness, anguish, torment, confusion, and suffering. Yes. I had stabbed my illness into James and watched it die with him. I no longer felt obedient... I felt... nothing... I was hollow...

I killed god. I am god.

I grabbed the charred meat from my plate, mindlessly pressed it to my heart- whether it was Jonah, my mother, or Superiorii Phorgiveness, didn't matter- turned around, walked towards the sheet of wood blocking the portal to the outside world, the world of the Fos Terata, your world, and moved it. Natural light was pouring in, shimmering against my bare toes. I was officially a portal. No redemption. Natural light had touched me. And it felt warm. It was beautiful. The light was good.

Printed in the USA
CPSIA information can be obtained
at www.ICGtesting.com
LVHW041003271223
767538LV00006B/197